Forests an
of the Adirondack
High Peaks Region

Forests and Trees of the Adirondack High Peaks Region

A Hiker's Guide

E.H. KETCHLEDGE

Adirondack Mountain Club
Lake George, New York

Published by the Adirondack Mountain Club Inc.
814 Goggins Road, Lake George, New York 12845-4117

Photographs by E.H. Ketchledge
Design by Cambridge Design Associates

Library of Congress Cataloging-in-Publication Data

Ketchledge, Edwin H.
Forests and Trees of the Adirondack High Peaks Region: a hiker's guide/ E.H. Ketchledge. — 3rd ed.
p. cm.
Includes bibliographical references and index.
ISBN 0-935272-49-6
1. Trees—New York (State)—Adirondack Mountains—Identification.
I. Title.
QK484.N7K47 1995
582.1609747'5—dc20 95-9177
CIP

Printed in the United States of America
10 9 8 7 6 5 4 99

PREFACE

In the Adirondacks, trees are always with us, wherever we go. They clothe the landscape in green finery; they provide shelter from the storm and give us shade during the heat of day. They capture our attention and grace our photographs. In their variety and combinations trees continually reveal and record changing forests that integrate the landscape and give distinct character to each mountain as we climb.

It seems appropriate, then, to pause awhile to make the acquaintance of these trees and their combinations that we walk among, to learn their kinds and their environments, and to share their natural history. With this knowledge comes a greater understanding of the ever-shifting forested landscape and, in turn, a deepened appreciation of our natural heritage in the Adirondack high peaks region.

E.H. Ketchledge

CONTENTS

The Adirondak Loj at Heart Lake. Within a few minutes of the Loj the walker can find twenty-six of the tree species described in this guide. Behind the Loj, at left, are Red and White Pine; at right, Balsam Fir; in front, Northern White-cedar.

INTRODUCTION

The diligent observer will find 34 species of trees in the high peak region of the Adirondack Mountains. Their numbers are about equally divided between conifers and hardwoods. Several are dominant trees, widely distributed throughout the mountains; a few are rare to these forests and may be found only with deliberate searching.

The purpose of this guide is to introduce hikers to the nature of the forests in the Adirondack high peak region (both the forested mountainsides and the valleys around and between them) and then to review the identity and ecology of the species of trees growing therein. It is not my intent to provide a scholarly discourse or a detailed study manual. Rather, I wish to interpret and explain the forests as a living landscape, constantly varying with the topography and environments, adjusting to past events, and responding to continuing modern pressures upon it. You will want to see both "who" is here and what is going on. In short, to read the landscape.[1]

THE FORESTS

Origins

The first step in interpreting the forested Adirondack landscape is understanding that what we view and enjoy today is but the latest version of several "Adirondacks" that developed and matured and then were overridden by re-advancing glaciers during the Pleistocene period, starting an estimated 1.5 million years ago. The latest glacier advance terminated 18,000 years ago and by 12,000 years ago glaciers had retreated from our region, leaving a debris-covered landscape open for forests and living creatures to reclaim once more. That process is still going on, as the returnees adjust both to natural forces and newer human impacts.

In that long-term context, we must interpret the Adirondack high peak region of today as part of an emerging landscape history, a region not yet fully recovered from the devastation wrought by continental glaciers (the last time around) and subject to continuing climatic and environmental shifts of all sorts. Curiously, part of that long history of numerous advances and retreats, driven by Earth's climatic changes, is now being revealed by ice cores drilled from the residual glaciers still persisting in Greenland and from sediment cores taken from Adirondack lakes, both of which contain a microscopic record of past events. Lesser climatic shifts continue into historical times and make us appreciate the fact that every majestic scene of the grand Adirondack high country that we enjoy today is but the latest version of a dynamic forest landscape continually responding to numerous environmental and ecological influences—in short, unfolding history.

A particular forest thus interpreted is both the multitude of living things that make up the biological community as it has developed over hundreds of years of time and the collective ecological forces and changes that operate to maintain that forested landscape in both space and time. In that perspective, a forested area is simultaneously the *product*, the physical phenomenon that we see with our eyes, and the *process*, the ecological forces we see with our minds.[2]

The newly bared landscape, exposed by the retreating glacial front in a warming climate, allowed another wave of plant and animal species to migrate northward from their glacial refugia further south and west, as had happened at least three times earlier in the Pleistocene during prolonged interglacial periods. The migration of tree species, each spreading at its own rate according to its ecological aggressiveness, continued until the warming reached a maximum intensity sometime prior to 6,000 years ago.

Once that ecological race was nearing completion and most of the tree species had arrived back in the Adirondacks, natural competition between species became the major factor determining the natural balance of early forest communities in the high peak region. Because heavy-seeded species such as American Beech migrate more slowly than do the species like birches and aspens, which have light, wind-blown seeds, not all returned to the high peak region at the same time: further, with the slightly cooling climate of the past few thousand years, even some of the speedy early arrivers were not everywhere fully at equilibrium with their habitats for hundreds of years.

Even today every natural community is a delicate balance among different species, each with its respective environmental requirements and each struggling with different competitive vigor, all in a changing world where growing conditions shift from time to time. The forests we see around us now are unique; they have no analogs in the past. Interglacial conditions have been here for only 40-tree generations of time. The outwardly stable forests we see in our human lifetime are more correctly understood as dynamic populations of competing species, adjusting as necessary over centuries of time to variations in the proverbial balance of nature: that so-called "balance" is more truthfully an episodic teeter-totter!

The record of vegetational return here and elsewhere is recorded in the fossilized sediments preserved either in the accumulated muck at the bottom of bogs or in the bottom sediments of small lakes such as Heart Lake, Upper Wallface Pond, and Lake Arnold, three of those that the Whitehead/Jackson team studied. Any pollen or plant parts (such as needles, twigs, or fruits) that fall into these quiet waters sink and become buried in the oxygen-depleted muck, where they may remain undecayed for thousands of years. Samples from such layers provide the evidence for reconstructing the time sequence of when the various species arrived at the location thousands of years ago. The bottom-most levels in the sediment "profile," as it is called, reveal who arrived first, just as subsequent deposits record who arrived next in the series. With modern radio-carbon dating technologies, we can also learn the approximate time each species in turn reached and occupied the area, much as is done in terrestrial archeological research.

We know that the first plants to arrive and establish themselves in the Heart Lake watershed 12,000 years ago were tundra-dwelling species, including Dwarf Birch, Alpine Bilberry and Crowberry, and especially Mountain Alder, all four of which still persist on the nearest alpine summit, Algonquin peak. Most of the more boreal (northern) species soon moved on, but about two dozen of them left offspring atop the alpine peaks in the high country.

Shortly, the first tree species, White Spruce, began to arrive, first in low numbers as scattered individuals, but by 10,800 years ago they formed spruce woodlands that probably resembled the stunted taiga forests of subarctic Canada today. From 9,000 to 7,000 years ago the spruce survived but soon became ill-adapted as the North American climates continued to warm, and in time they disappeared. Prior to the spruce slowdown and withdrawal, however, Balsam Fir appeared on the scene and has held on continuously at higher elevations where it remains today the primary species near and below timberline.

White Pine appears in the Heart Lake record at 9,000 years ago, and from 8,400 to 6,000 years ago it was an important component in the mixed hardwood-conifer forest that was developing in the local watershed. At 7,400 years ago, Eastern Hemlock arrived and spread rapidly, replacing the pine and becoming the most abundant conifer in the region; soon, however, it went into a remarkably sharp decline everywhere in the northeastern states-to-be, becoming the first "forest decline" on records. It remained absent until about 3,400 years ago, when it finally returned, never achieving its earlier abundance.

Hardwood species, of course, were similarly returning to the region over this time period. Paper Birch was the first, as might be expected, arriving at 10,000 years ago. It remained the only broad-leaved species in abundance until the Thermal Maximum Period, about 6,000 years ago when the warming period peaked; by this time, many hardwood species had arrived back in the Adirondacks, most notably our three most characteristic ones, Yellow Birch, Sugar Maple and American Beech.

With the decline of the hemlock, and as regional climates started to turn cool again, Yellow Birch expanded in numbers. That ecological shift also marks a major biological change in Adirondack forest composition, because that was when Red Spruce appeared on the scene, as if out of nowhere, and quickly became the dominant conifer in the Adirondack Mountains. Indeed, that is when Adirondack forests took on their presettlement appearance, organization, and ecology.

The fossil records from Upper Wallface Pond and Lake Arnold (representing the highest country) differ somewhat from that of Heart Lake because of the environmental factors associated with their higher elevations, particularly the cooler climate, of course, but also the prevalence of acid, organic soils in the high country versus the richer glacial tills down below. The highest slopes were dominated by Balsam Fir and Paper Birch once the early spruce departed and remained so until the arrival of Red Spruce up to the 4000-ft. level where the mineral soils ran out. Small populations of Black Spruce cling on, contorted at tree line and dwarfed in the alpine meadows of several of the highest summits, where boggy soils give them the competitive advantage. The early pioneering

White Spruce gave up the slopes entirely and is now sporadically present only on level ground at the base of the high peaks. As a forest ecologist who has spent half a century studying Adirondack forests, I still find it amazing to think that our Red Spruce—such a dominating species in virgin Adirondack forests of pre-colonial times—did not arrive here and become so prominently established until 2,000 years ago.

The sequence outlined here is based upon pollen and actual plant parts, which are called "macrofossils." A corresponding profile can also be constructed using "microfossils," especially the minute valves or microscopic shells of diatom algae in sediments of the same three high peaks lakes, as also studied by Dr. Donald F. Charles and associates.[3] The microfossils provide valuable additional information and interpretation because the various species, by their combinations and abundance, tell us much about the chemistry of their home waters and watershed forests. Most importantly, because of their chemistry requirements, their presence reveals an "inferred pH" that can be used to construct the alkalinity/acidity history of the lake. Admittedly, the interpretation is less exact than that for physical macrofossil, but it still reveals major environmental trends that influence plant abundance over time in the watershed.

Surprisingly, the inferred pH of Heart Lake early after the glaciers left was circumneutral, in fact slightly above 7.0 pH. So, too, for Upper Wallface Pond and Lake Arnold, where alders were among the first invaders to arrive in the early tundra phase. Alders are nitrogen-fixing plants that improve soil fertility. In time the pH at Heart Lake dropped to about 6.0 as the surrounding slopes became clothed in a forest cover of, first, White Spruce and Balsam Fir, then Eastern Hemlock, all three species of which drop acidic leaf litter that in turn produces a soil of lower pH. Even rainfall dripping through the coniferous foliage becomes acidic. Acidic runoff from the forest slopes soon reduced the Heart Lake pH a corresponding amount.

With the arrival of the hardwoods once the regional climate had warmed up during the middle of the post-glacial period, and with the disappearance of the hemlock, the lake pH stabilized at 6.0. But later, with the return of the hemlock and then the Red Spruce, plus the continuing Balsam Fir in the watershed, the water pH dropped to about 5.5, the lowest it has ever been in Pleistocene post-glacial history. Over the past 1,500 years the pH trend has reversed. The lake chemistry has risen back to 6.6, apparently in response to an increasing predominance of the hardwoods over the conifers at the lower elevations. Additionally, there has been an increase in the prevalence of forest fires in this century, which tend to neutralize the soils via wood ashes and soon increase the pH of nearby waters as well. The point of this digression into forest and lake chemistry is that the vegetation itself has an impact on the environment, and as one changes the other may shift accordingly. The trees influence the process.

If we superimpose upon these long-term climatic shifts and vegetational responses the more frequent lesser cycles or periodic perturbations in climate, such as the Little Ice Age of recent centuries, we come to appreciate the environmental disharmonies enforced on forests and their species everywhere. Add to that the occasional killing extremes in weather, or flooding, or insect or fungal attacks on particular species. No year is without some impact on some species or some locale of the forest community. Less obvious but equally important are the subtle longer term cycles in climate which may enhance or diminish the vigor of individual species, particularly the more southern species which in the Adirondacks have reached the northern limits of their ranges.

In effect, then, a forest quivers in time, always in lag to its changing environment, always seeking equilibrium via the separate dynamics of its constituent species, collectively adjusting to the changing environment that it in part creates by growth and to the external environment over which it has no control, the whole community of plants responding in consort, on time frames measured in decades and centuries. The movement of animals is measured in geography; that of forests, in time.

Product and process, community and environment linked in interactions: the very organization, composition, and ecology of our pre-colonial Adirondack forests were determined in large measure by these pre-historical dynamics long before we arrived in North America. Just how, we will examine next.

Glacial Heritage

As we accumulate experiences exploring the Adirondack countryside, we soon realize that certain tree species seem to form loose associations that repeat themselves from place to place whenever similar environmental conditions occur. Often these forests are temporary kinds of stands with many different species present, such as those that follow logging or wildfires, which in time give way to the climax forests that persist into the future. Others may be less disturbed and less diverse sub-climax stands slowly approaching balance with their habitat. In New York State some 30 such repeating "Forest Types" are recognized by the Society of American Foresters and serve as guidelines for preparing management practices and procedures in commercial/production forests. Ultimately, however, on time scales of a century or more, these temporary Forest Types, many created by recent human disturbance, converge toward one generalized kind of forest characteristic of each of the five major forest environmental/ecological systems in the Adirondack Mountains.

Within the Adirondack uplands, here meaning (arbitrarily) lands above 1200-ft. elevation, the complex topography and specialized ecology therein limits the kinds of trees present to about 32 northern hardwoods and northern conifers; another 30 warmer-climate species occur in the lowlands surrounding the park but are infrequent on higher ground and thus excluded from this review. Further, the distribution of each of the 32 native Adirondack species differs across the highlands according to its individual needs and tolerances. Some withstand the colder climates in the upper elevations, others get along best on sunny slopes near the base of the mountains. Some species require continually wet soils, and others survive droughty locations without damage. Some prefer deep mineral soils, others get along fine on organic soils.

In effect, the pattern of regional environments seems to act like an ecological sieve, only allowing a few of the species to grow vigorously and become competitive at any particular location. The theoretical balance of nature thus varies from place to place across the high peak region, with different combinations of species thriving most successfully over the years in particular settings. Where seeds happen to fall on unfavorable habitats or sites for that species, the seedlings will eventually disappear without reproducing.

In the Adirondack region this ecological selection process seems to produce five major groupings of tree species that repeat themselves from place to place. These generalized groupings of selected species corresponding to major regional habitats are called "site-types" (see chart, p. 21). In the high peaks, site–types seem to correspond most closely to the two major environmental gradients, elevation and topography. In sequence of decreasing elevation, they are:

- the Spruce/Fir Site-Type on cold middle and high mountainsides,
- the Hardwood Site-Type on warm and fertile low slopes,
- the Mixed Woods Site-Type on warm and infertile low slopes,
- the Pine Site-Type on droughty glacial moraines,
- the Spruce Swamp Site-Type on saturated lowland soils.

The value of the concept of site-types to the observant hiker is that it enables us to interpret the different kinds of forests we encounter when exploring the high peaks. If we know the tree species and their characteristics, we can match them to the landscape and see if they match one of the five theoretical site-types generally recognized by foresters and ecologists. On a steep, high mountainside, for example, we know that young Balsam Fir saplings coming up under a canopy of Paper Birch will eventually

ADIRONDACK FOREST SITE–TYPES

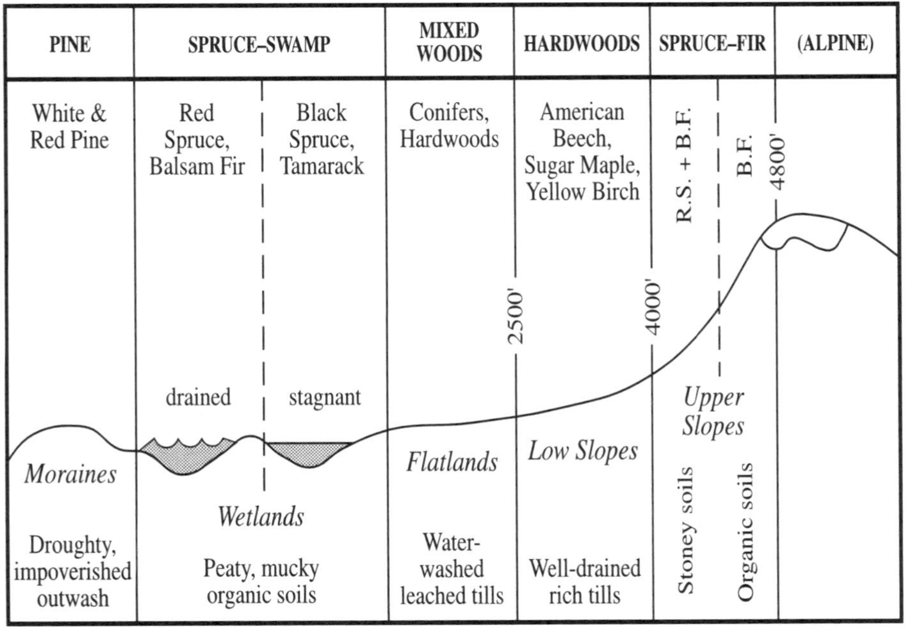

PINE	SPRUCE–SWAMP		MIXED WOODS	HARDWOODS	SPRUCE–FIR		(ALPINE)
White & Red Pine	Red Spruce, Balsam Fir	Black Spruce, Tamarack	Conifers, Hardwoods	American Beech, Sugar Maple, Yellow Birch	R.S. + B.F.	B.F.	
	drained	stagnant	2500'	4000'		4800'	
Moraines	*Wetlands*		*Flatlands*	*Low Slopes*	*Upper Slopes*		
Droughty, impoverished outwash	Peaty, mucky organic soils		Water-washed leached tills	Well-drained rich tills	Stoney soils	Organic soils	

take over the site and shade out any new Paper Birch seedlings, thus restoring the forest to the climax status that preceded a forest fire long ago. Thus we can add even further enjoyment to our walks and climbs in the high peak region by playing "ecologist" whenever the topography changes sharply and speculating on the nature of the primeval forests that once greeted our forefathers in the early 1800s and toward which the now oft-disturbed forests are slowly returning.

To understand the ecological nature of our five fundamental Adirondack forest site-types, we must go back to the time when melting glaciers freed up the Adirondacks from their Pleistocene ice-locked sleep. The rocky debris carried by the continental glaciers as they scraped off the landscape for over a hundred thousand years was eventually dropped in place as the melting glacier front retreated northward, starting 18,000 years ago. The glacial debris, called "till," consisted of all kinds of soil, ranging in size from tiny clay and silt particles up to large rocks and giant boulders. Over the subsequent decades and centuries as world climates warmed and the glacial front melted and retreated northward, forests slowly seeded northward also, back into their former territory. Meanwhile, most of the glacial till left on mountain tops washed off the summits and high ridges, leaving bare bedrock atop the highest peaks. The high summit islands of landscape in time became a lasting world of mosses and lichens and tundra vegetation, a living heritage and museum of post-glacial times, similar to that of high latitudes in northern Canada today.

The highest slopes below the mountain tops, down to about the 4000-ft. level, retain at best only a thin mantle of glacial debris;

the shallow soils there consist primarily of decomposed organic material produced by the remains of post-glacial tundra, shrubs, and dwarfed trees barely clinging to life in severe sub-alpine environments, where even the decay process is slowed into centuries. The black organic soils we see exposed along the eroding trails in the high country date from the days when the glaciers first departed the Adirondack high country. Today this is the subalpine landscape of the short-lived Balsam Fir, the climax species, and Mountain Paper Birch, the pioneering species: a whole forest ecosystem reduced essentially to just two short-lived tree species. In the Adirondack Park this is seen extensively only in the high peak region of the northeastern sector or occasionally elsewhere on steep or exposed slopes of lesser mountains.

Further downslope to about the 2500-ft. level, the shallow soil mantle retains most of the stony debris left by the glaciers, though on these steep slopes much of the fertile silts and clays were washed away long ago. Further, the soils are continuously moist due to the regular seepage (at times flow) of rainwater over the impervious bedrock a foot or so below the soil surface. These cool and moist mid-slopes of modest fertility provide a suitable home for the long-lived Red Spruce as well, so now the forest is dominated by a higher canopy of Red Spruce with an understory of shorter-lived Balsam Fir and Paper Birch, together constituting a spruce/fir forest type. At elevations under 3500 feet Yellow Birch occurs also but only in low numbers, often growing, however, to large size; its presence is dependent upon occasional breaks in the forest canopy caused by natural ecological disturbances.

These two mountainside forest types constitute two elevational versions of the **Spruce/Fir Site-Type** (in the older literature often called the "Upper Spruce Slope") and differ primarily in having organic soils in the high-slope portion and coarse mineral soils in the mid-slope elevations. Further, the progressive decrease in size of trees up toward the timberline reveals increasing severity of the weather and the difficult growing conditions in these cold and wind-battered environments of high mountainsides. Indeed, the Balsam Fir and Mountain Paper Birch prove to be among the most cold-hardy trees in the Adirondacks, much as they are in the high boreal latitudes of Canada. The two dominating conifers of the Spruce/Fir Site-Type, with their somber green coloration, characterize the old-growth conditions in the Adirondack high country, whereas modern second-growth stands, with their characteristic light-green reflections as seen from nearby mountaintops, attest to the role of vigorous Paper Birch filling in any gaps occurring in the spruce/fir canopy.

On the lower and warmer mountainsides, the deeper soil mantle retains the full spectrum of soil particles, so these best of fertile sites support pure hardwood forests or hardwoods with only a minor admixture of conifers. Indeed, such gentle slopes of lesser mountains dominate the Adirondack forested landscape and cover most of the park. A typical soil profile here will show a gradual blending of "horizons" or fertility levels from the blackish humus layer at top downward over two or three feet of rich, brown soil to the unweathered and thus paler parent glacial debris below, a sure indicator of long, undisturbed weathering and mineral accumulation on the site. In the original Adirondack forest, some shade-tolerant Red Spruce and Eastern Hemlock trees hung on in these stands as lesser admixtures, but the faster-growing hardwoods always seemed to outgrow and out-compete their coniferous brethren. The hardwood forests, of course, are recognized immediately by their bright green foliage that seems to dominate practically all of the southern and central Adirondack Park today.

A different post-glacial history, though, has affected much of the low hill portions of the Adirondacks, especially the northwestern third of the region, a lasting effect actually from late glacial times. There on the more level flatlands and rolling plateau topography, flooding glacier meltwaters so churned and tumbled and washed the glacial till after it was deposited that most of the fine-grained silts and clays (which store essential minerals) were often washed away down the rivers to the Atlantic, several thousand years before we arrived on the scene. These "water-washed" soils, as they are called, that surround all the major river systems in those parts of the modern park are so depleted in nutrients that few demanding hardwoods can survive. Further, being so low-lying on the landscape, soils here are often water-logged, an additional stress for the demanding deciduous-leaved species. In this geographical region, often of too much water and too little soil fertility, the conifers typically gain control or share dominance with the hardwoods.

On the lowest sites where the water tends to be stagnant, as in many forested wetlands around the high peaks, Black Spruce and Tamarack survive, in fact seem to thrive given the absence of competitors. Freshwater situations such as along meandering streams, however, bring a better balance of minerals and oxygen, and here Red Spruce and Balsam Fir typically dominate the area. Curiously,

Northern White-cedar may occur sporadically on hummocks in either situation. On nearby flat ground elevated only a few feet above the water table, nearly pure stands of Red Spruce outlasted the other species and became the "Spruce Flats" so prized by the early loggers. All of these spruce-dominated wetland forests are called the **Spruce Swamp Site-Type**. As a rule of thumb, the more Red Spruce you see in these wetland situations, the fresher the water; the more Black Spruce outnumbers the red, the more stagnant the water. From the air or a distant mountain, the spruces and their associated Balsam Fir give a somber green cast to the lowlands of the northwest sector of the park, matching the green of the Spruce-Fir Site–Type in the high country. So, too, in the watersheds around and draining our major lakes across the park, with conifers on the lowest, wettest ground and hardwoods off to the sides of the wetlands on the better drained, gentle slopes.

Meanwhile, a distinct transition zone always seems to occur over the first hundred feet or so of elevation up on to drier ground where hardwoods dominate the forest cover. This persistent transition zone of forests seems to closely follow the immediate local topography, where the soils are still the water-washed type depleted of nutrients but, being slightly elevated, are now drained of excess moisture. Given these in-between environmental conditions, a mixture of various hardwoods and conifers now reaches a competitive balance: Red Spruce and Balsam Fir continue on and are joined by abundant Eastern Hemlock, but Red Maple, Yellow Birch and a few other hardwoods also join in. And wherever small rises or depressions occur in the topography, or wherever side streams or ravine join the primary system, other tree species find suitable habitat. Given the resulting diversity (complexity!) in forest composition, these locations are called simply the **Mixed Woods Site-Type.** Although their ecology and geography may appear confusing at first, such vast lands of gentle and accessible landscape were highly important in earlier times as they produced much of the coniferous timber that was once so heavily removed from Adirondack forests. Meanwhile, conifers do not regenerate via stump sprouts, as do most hardwoods. They return to a former site only by seed dispersal from undisturbed distant forests, during which time the residual hardwood canopy shades out most conifer seedlings. The return of conifers to shared canopy dominance in Mixed Woods stands is typically a matter of centuries.

For these ecological reasons, the hardwoods there now outnumber the conifers by a large ratio. Consequently, the residual stands of now-pure hardwoods left on the logged Mixed-Woods slopes near the wetlands today blend imperceptibly upslope into the always-pure **Hardwood Site-Type** occupying the richer low and middle slope terrain that escaped the water-washing from melting glaciers of long ago. History is at work here, confusing the inherent ecological distinction between the Mixed Woods Site-Type on the lower areas of the terrain (with their depleted water-washed tills) and the Hardwood Site-Type upslope on higher ground (with their rich unsorted tills). Blame it on the loggers, who harvested mostly conifers.

The current visitor can distinguish between the two blending site–types in two ways: First, the original Hardwood Site-Type was dominated by Sugar Maple and American Beech, the two long-lived climax species, and Yellow Birch, a characteristic invader following disturbances. Few conifers other than some Red Spruce and Eastern Hemlock could withstand the dense shade cast by the hardwood canopy. Even today, the understory remains one of young beech/maple hardwoods; few sun-loving hardwood species can survive. By contrast, Red Spruce and Eastern Hemlock seedlings gradually infiltrate into the understory layer on the Mixed–Wood Site–Types wherever sunlight breaks through the canopy.

Second, the soil profiles of the two site-types are quite different. If you dig a hole in the ground in a Hardwood Site-Type, you see a very gradual change in coloration the deeper you go, often to 3 feet deep. On the other hand, the soil chemistry under conifers of a Mixed Woods is acid: as the organic debris slowly decays, the acids thereby produced leach the soluble minerals from the top of the till layer immediately below, leaving behind a conspicuous band of white sand between the black organic layer at top and the brownish layer of rich till below. In many cases just kicking the ground is enough to expose the white sand layer, 1 to 4 inches thick, typical of the Mixed–Woods Site–Type. For that matter, the white sand layer is often exposed by erosion on the banks of the many access trails into the high peaks, such as into Marcy Dam, Johns Brook Valley, or the Dixes.

Because on gradual slopes the transition from Mixed-Woods into Hardwoods is often indistinct, foresters have learned to check by looking for Balsam Fir: if it is present in the understory around you, your are usually in the lower Mixed–Woods portion of the slope; if it is absent, you are probably in the higher Hardwood Site–Type. Further, Sugar Maple, being a nutrient-demanding, rich-soils species, is relatively infrequent on the mineral-depleted and water-washed soils of the Mixed-Woods, even though some American Beech and Yellow Birch are often present.

Since the typical crown of the evergreen component, if any, in this site-type is narrow and spire-like (whereas the hardwood canopies are broad and wide-spreading), it is the bright green reflection of the Sugar Maples and their hardwood cohorts that we see when viewing this site-type from afar. When viewed from a plane, the three elevational color zones of northern Adirondack Mountains—the dark green of the meandering lowland river systems and the high spruce/fir mountainsides separated by the light green of the vast hill country between and all around in every direction—create a strong and lasting visual impact.

One more important forest site-type remains conspicuous across the northern Adirondack landscape: wherever slightly elevated gravelly glacial moraines stick up above the wetlands so that their ground surface is above the water table, the pines thrive vigorously even with low soil fertility and are thus often considered a separate if temporary **Pine Site-Type** distinct from the rest of the Mixed Woods to which these habitats eventually return. The best examples are seen on meandering eskers left by the glaciers or on dry, droughty ridges and sand plains. Here they form the tallest stands in the park, with some individual trees reaching over 130 feet in height.

As a group, the pines are all drought-resistant because of the very fast growth of their main tap root the first several seasons, which allows them to get established quickly on either rocky or dry moraines or on dry sandy plains. For similar reasons they may be seen on shallow soils or rocky ridges or bluffs where water still drains over the bedrock. Whenever you see a patch of dark green conifers growing on an otherwise very steep hardwood-covered mountainside, that is a spot of shallow but periodically moistened soil where pines (and even Red Spruce) will flourish in the absence of less demanding competitors. For similar reasons, both because of early fast growth and ability to grow vigorously on infertile mineral soils, the Eastern White Pine proved to be the most successful pioneering tree after forest harvesting on the drier east side of the Adirondacks. Just drive the Northway from Lake George north to the high peak region: admixtures of White Pine are constantly in view.

In modern times the underlying ecological logic, so to speak, of the primeval Adirondack forests has been obscured by the last century and a half of disruptive logging, which has produced a confusing pattern of temporary "Forest Types" as numerous tree species compete for dominance in the newly created forest openings, be they small patches or whole hillsides. Each one of the several sites-types we here describe is capable of supporting alternate combinations of fast-growing pioneering tree species for about a hundred years, but by that time the shaded understory is comprised of shade-tolerant climax species, replacing the sun-requiring pioneering tree species that had exploited the sunny ground a century or two ago. Sure, dozens of tree species may happen to seed into any new forest clearing created by logging activities, but once that first wave of pioneers has shaded the site again, only the few species tolerant of the shaded environment will survive long enough to reproduce their kinds. Every site-type thus has its own combination of growing conditions on which only a selected few of the 32 (in the high peak region) available species can long survive. Those temporary "successional" forests on once-disturbed lands are today fast reverting toward their respective primeval site-type status in most of the Forest Preserve.

Many of us hiking Adirondack trails find it fun to identify trees along the route. If you know your species, and if you know your approximate position on the local countryside, you can see whether or not the trees match the site. If the understory species are the same kinds as those in the canopy, you are probably in an old-growth forest characteristic of one of the five site-types. If they are different, forest succession is going on, and your grandchildren in their time will see a different forest type at that location. With a little visual examination you may be able to predict what the future forest may be like. Just keep in mind that each location may show a different combination of species depending upon the severity of past disturbances and on the local ecological conditions. Given enough years, though, forest composition at every location converges toward mature stands in which about a dozen dominant and shade-tolerant species perpetuate themselves indefinitely; that is, until another disturbance in the environment or community—such as the appearance of European immigrants in the northern Adirondacks nearly two hundred years ago—initiates a new cycle of recovery.

Historical Impacts

By historical impacts we mean those things humans have done to the forested landscape, most of which are matters of record. For the purposes of this guide we identify some well-known areas and examples of kinds of disturbances you will see in hiking the trail system rather than giving a sequential or complete catalog of human disturbances to the forested landscape of the high peak region. Our purpose is to alert you to the fact that in addition to the glacial and ancient migratory histories that produced the precolonial conditions reported above, most of what you see in the high peak region today is in some stage of recovery from historical events of the past two centuries. The high peaks wilderness area is today more accurately a wilderness-to-be. About 80 to 85 percent of the forested landscape has experienced one or more impacts from human activities in the course of the past two centuries. Although it is now difficult to provide details of which stands experienced what particular disturbances and at what intensities, we modern-day visitors must accept the fact that on any trip to a high summit we pass mostly through disturbed countryside where two or three generations of loggers once harvested the trees and where, too often, subsequent forest fires further destroyed evidence of the great primeval forests that once characterized the virgin Adirondacks. Excluding any discussion of land clearance in the surrounding flatlands, first for agriculture and then urbanization, we will focus here on the landscape still clothed in forest cover today.

At the start of the 19th century, when the first land surveyors, explorers, and settlers were arriving in the high peak region, the virgin forests in the northern parts of the Adirondacks were close to a 50:50 balance of softwoods:hardwoods. In the annual report of the Forest Commission for 1895, the Superintendent of State Forests, William F. Fox, reports that studies in the Floodwood area north of Saranac Lake show Red Spruce constituting 35 percent of the forest trees, Eastern Hemlock 15 percent, and Balsam Fir 3 percent; American Beech, Yellow Birch and Sugar Maple constituted the rest of the stands. The sample sites were on commercial forests lands of modest relief and did not include the less valuable but more diverse successional or disturbance stands in which other Adirondack tree species find their place in the forest ecosystem. Another study of four stands of virgin, primitive forests near Roaring Brook, a mountainside area near Keene Valley, also showed conifers as 50 percent of the forest trees. This was the type of country that attracted lumbermen, who were seeking softwood species whose logs or bolts could be floated to the mills for pulp.

Red Spruce was the prized species sought by the lumbermen, as it occurred in high numbers up to about 4000 ft. elevation, where Balsam Fir began to replace it as the canopy species. Although stands were clearcut of their mature large trees, the younger understory ones were left; many such stands are fast returning to their old-growth condition. On the other hand, young balsam grows faster than spruce, so most of these stands now have an ascending canopy of the Balsam Fir with an understory of more fir and Red Spruce slowly coming up beneath. Such can be seen on the slopes of Seward and Seymour in the Cold River country and up to the cliffs of Big Slide Mountain in the Johns Brook Valley; this phenomenon of temporary one-generation dominance replacement of spruce by balsam is characteristic of much of the high country that was logged in the first two decades of this century. In many of these stands Paper Birch also got a big boost in numbers since it is a fast "exploiter" tree, a pioneer that explodes in numbers immediately after natural or human disturbances, responding even quicker than the Balsam Fir. Fortunately, although this was mostly steep up-and-down country being logged, the fact that the logs/bolts were removed by horses rather than machinery, and removal was done in winter with sleds, prevented serious ecological damage to the landscape. Even today the bushwhacker may occasionally run across some old cribbing or corduroy that records these former activities.[4]

Meanwhile, logging was going on elsewhere in the high peak region during these first two decades of the 20th century. During the 1913–15 period, forty loggers were working on the MacIntyre Range and another seventy near Scotts Dam and Scotts Pond (highest logging pond in the state of New York) in the Indian Pass sector. (Curiously, to my knowledge no one has ever made a systematic archaeological study of those old lumbering camps in the high country.) Over a hundred men lived and worked in the Cold River country, and forty lived at a lumbering camp at Dix Pond in 1914, when the Elk Lake region was logged as far north as the high slopes on the west side of Dix Mountain. An occasional piece of abandoned machinery still attests to their presence long ago.

In the Giant–Hopkins Peak area, clear-cut logging continued up to 3500 ft. elevation until about 1924 and was much heavier and more damaging to the forest. At about this time the state of

New York began buying back lands within the central high peaks region, whether logged or uncut, and region-wide logging essentially ceased. (Some lands on the southwest border of the high peaks remain in commercial ownership with Finch Pruyn, who earlier in 1914–15 had been logging around Calamity Brook and Upper Twin Brook. Similarly, International Paper had logged the Preston Ponds area, driving their logs down the Cold and Raquette Rivers to Tupper Lake.) The days of forest exploitation were over, but another threat had appeared in the footsteps of the loggers: forest fires.

Forest fires were historically rare events in the relatively wet climate of the northeastern states as opposed to their frequent occurrence in the drier midwestern states. But with the drying slash left over and accumulating from timber harvesting, wild fires became new and devastating impacts in various sections of the central and northern Adirondacks and high peaks region.[5]

Regional fires hit the high peak region significantly starting in the spring of 1903. Local fires swept from South Meadows and Mt. Jo southward past Marcy Dam to Phelps Mt., up the northeast edge of the MacIntyre mountains, and eastward over Pitchoff, Cascade, and Porter. Another major fire burned westward from the Underwood area up the east slopes of Macomb and Dix, then northward to Noonmark and Chapel Pond. Another spread over much of Rocky Peak Ridge, Giant and Green Mt. In 1906 the northeast slopes of Hurricane burned, as did Jay. In the fall of 1913 fires returned to portions of the 1903 burns near Dix, Rocky Peak, and Giant Mt., producing grassy slopes for a number of years. And so the story went, in this second-worst year for forest fires in the Adirondack Mountains.

In most cases the scarred landscape soon revegetated, in some instances (as on Macomb) going through a grass stage before the trees returned. In others, the pioneering tree species soon raised a new canopy over the blackened landscape. When you stand on Dix Peak in the early fall as hardwood leaves are turning color, and you look northwestward to the Dial–Nippletop ridge, you see a pattern of gold and green: once-burned lands have become a golden-yellow tapestry, reflected by the canopy of pioneering Paper Birch now contrasting with the somber dark green of the nearby spruce/fir forests. Better yet, stand on Algonquin. Here, looking west to the tops of Street and McNaughton, you see the pattern of scattered gold amongst the dark green balsam, typical of the natural subalpine scene. Then turn to look more northward to the slopes of Nye, where you will see the red/orange of maples that, following logging, have temporarily spread high up on the deforested slopes left by the loggers in 1913–15. One of the most dramatic fall views is looking from Wright Peak eastward to Phelps and seeing the vast golden landscape extending over to Cascade and Porter. A view from Wright Peak in winter, looking down to Heart Lake, shows a similar contrast: the rusty brown twigs of the Paper Birch that came in on the northeast slope of Wright after the 1903 fires. Fall is the best time to stand on a high summit and visually scour the high country landscape for signs of disturbance to the dark evergreen canopy. They will reveal to you which forest areas have a story to tell.

Here we should mention two other dramatic disruptions to the high-country forest canopy, one a natural phenomenon, the other due to human activity: "fir waves" and spruce decline. Fir waves are the patches of blowdown in mature forest stands of Balsam Fir in the subalpine forests below timberline.[6] The Balsam Fir grows in pure stands, and when these trees reach maturity and become senescent at 80–90 years, they succumb to persistent high winds and die off in blocks. The surviving upslope trees forming the edge of the opening then take the full blast of the winds, and they too soon die, thereby enlarging the opening. Meanwhile, on the protected downslope edge, in the eddy of wind, new balsam seedlings spring up. Over the decades the opening seems to move upslope, with the upper edge retreating by death of mature trees and the downslope edge advancing upward by growth of the young ones. The process is very conspicuous looking north and eastward from Marcy over Tabletop and from Whiteface over toward Esther.

Meanwhile, further downslope in the spruce zone below 4000 ft. elevation, one sees hundreds of Red Spruce trees either dead or dying, due to annual loss of green foliage. This is a slow dieback apparently related in part to modern-day atmospheric pollution, to which Red Spruce seems to be very susceptible. In short, it seems that the polluted air delays or depresses the spruce's ability to go dormant on schedule in the fall, thus making it especially susceptible to damage from early, severe frosts or freezing weather in October or November. The damage here exhibits no pattern; rather, all trees may be impacted by the same episode of early freezing cold fronts. My own observation is that essentially all the Red Spruce in the Adirondack high country has been severely damaged or killed by the problem, but that for the last five spring seasons the survivors have not shown the typical browned needles that previously foretold their eventual fate. (It takes about two decades for the trees to succumb.) Hopefully, the legislation to tighten up the Clean Air Act a few years ago is paying off. Meanwhile, the associated understory species in these stands, particularly Balsam Fir and Paper Birch, have filled in any canopy gaps and the forest canopy remains continuous. In effect, these impacted stands show a shift in importance of the several composing species which will take perhaps two hundred years to overcome, due to the normally slow growth of the dominating Red Spruce. So the future may be assured in the spruce/fir forest, but we must pay the price of two centuries' time for "old-growth" conditions to arrive. Meanwhile, we now turn to the question of forest tree dynamics and see how that future comes about, given all the impacts humans have created in the forests of the high peak region.

Recovering Forests

Approximately 80 species of trees grow in the forests of New York State. About 60 of them reach the margins of the Adirondack Mountain uplands at one place or another, mostly along the lowlands of major rivers draining the region, where warmer climates permit their partial penetration into the governmentally defined "Adirondack Park."[7] Further, because each species has different environmental requirements of its own, each has a slightly different abundance and vigor across that range, determined by the immediate habitat conditions. In truth, the forest, so uniform in outward appearance, differs gradually but significantly in both tree composition and tree vitality across the major environmental gradients present in the region. Note, for example, that those 60 tree species at the margin of the park gradually, one by one, drop out as you climb to a high alpine summit, where just two cold-hardy species, Balsam Fir and Paper Birch, are left to form a final timberline. The same phenomenon to a lesser degree is silently happening along the moisture gradients, from bog- or streamside upslope to the dry cliff faces—or along the exposure gradient from the sunny south-facing side of a mountain around the contour level to the shaded and cooler north-facing slope.

On any particular site, a certain species we might expect to be present is infrequent or absent because the soil is too acid for it there. Or if present, it may be growing poorly because the site happens to be a frost pocket, subject to temperature extremes during critical periods of its growth. The fact of forest life is that every site is slightly different from every other one, which ecological reality, of course, creates the biological diversity we prize in our Adirondack landscape. In general, it is the broad pattern of regional climate, topography, drainage, and soils that determines the kinds of forest associations and site–types we see across the park today.

Equally as important as understanding the changes in the forest over periods of time is understanding the *dynamics* of tree species—that is, how they continually interact with each other and how they respond to their changing environment over their own lifetime as the forest matures and a canopy closes over the top of the community. Individual tree species respond differently because they differ in "tolerance"—the degree to which they can withstand ecological competition with their neighbors. Some trees, such as Quaking Aspen and Paper Birch, will not grow well if shaded by other trees around them, whether of their own kind or of other species. If shaded, they gradually slow down in growth and may die out; their seedlings are found only in open areas, rarely under an existing tree canopy. These species are called *intolerant*. On the other hand, trees such as Sugar Maple and American Beech grow well in competition with other trees; they tolerate shade and, as seedlings, continue to grow under a dense forest canopy. We call such species *tolerant*, meaning they have the ability to remain vigorous when growing in mixture with other species and are able to perpetuate themselves in mature stands.

Most tree species fall somewhere between these extremes and are classified as *mid-tolerant* or intermediate in tolerance. The significance of tree tolerance is that it helps to explain either the changes that occur in a forest following a disturbance or the absence of change after the canopy has closed over the site.

When a forest is cleared or burned or a field abandoned, the land is invaded by intolerant species that require the full sunlight of open areas. As the early pioneering species invade and grow larger and begin to shade the site, they render it unsuitable for their own seedlings. Mid-tolerant species capable of growing in partial shade then take over the area for a period of decades, and as their canopy gradually closes over the site they, too, give way, this time to the tolerant species capable of growing and reproducing in the densest shade. In such mature stands the sunlight on the forest floor may be reduced to just 2 percent of full sunlight, conditions wherein only Red Spruce and Eastern Hemlock among the conifers and Sugar Maple and American Beech among the hardwoods are able to survive until some natural breaks in the canopy enable the stand to resume its normal growth.

The whole process of going from a logged-over landscape back to a mature "old-growth" forest may take several hundred years; a canopy of pioneering species may rise over the ground in fifty years or so, but it will take another hundred years or more for the climax species to appear in that canopy and then another hundred or two for their kin to displace the aging subclimax trees still holding on. Natural changes come about slowly, and may even be delayed or set back on any particular site by new natural disturbances such as hurricanes or wild fires.

The gradual replacement of tree species upon a site is called "plant succession." As species or groups of species invade and occupy a site, they modify the environment and establish new ecological conditions that may initiate still another invasion by other species better adapted to the changed condition. The successive waves of tree populations eventually slow down as a stable environment develops under the canopy. This end product of vegetational development is called the "climax" forest—the mature, long-lasting association of trees in natural balance with the environment. So long as the forest is undisturbed by outside influences, the climax association will occupy the site over several tree generations until it, too, loses vigor because of changes induced on the site, such as leaf litter shifting the soil chemistry to higher or lower levels. Such subtle changes may shift the relative dominance of species, as happened to our forests in late glacial times when the abundance of conifers in the high peak region caused a slight acidification of the soils. Many hidden but long-lasting changes are still going on in primeval stands—but at rates slower than the human lifetime.

All sorts of disturbances have occurred and are occurring in the high peak region, and in consequence we see a great diversity of forest conditions: different species, in various stages of health, vigor, and form, from pure stands of one species to mixed stands containing many species; tall, lordly trees on fertile, undisturbed sites to dwarfed, contorted specimens at timberline; different stages of revegetation reflecting a particular history of use or abuse. In hindsight it may be a story of mismanagement, but it also provides an intriguing case study for the person interested in forest recovery and the responses of a variety of tree species to varying environmental treatments and conditions.

Endnotes

[1] For directions on how to prepare a leaf collection of the many tree species for further study at home, write the Extension Office, State University of New York College of Environmental Science and Forestry, Syracuse, NY, 13210, and ask for a copy of *Plant Collecting: A Guide to the Preparation of a Plant Collection.*

[2] For a technical discussion of post-glacial forest return, see *The Regional Vegetational History of the High Peaks (Adirondack Mountains), New York*, New York State Museum Bulletin No. 478, by Donald R. Whitehead and Stephen T. Jackson, New York

State Museum, Albany, New York, 1990; and *Postglacial Vegetational Changes along an Elevational Gradient in the Adirondack Mountains (New York). A Study of Plant Macrofossils*, Biological Survey/State Museum Bulletin 465, by Stephen T. Jackson, New York State Museum, Albany, New York, 1989. For an excellent summary, see pp. 10–11 in *The Great Forest of the Adirondacks*, by Barbara McMartin, North Country Books, Utica, New York, 1994.

3 *Late-Glacial and Holocene Acidity Changes in Adirondack (N.Y.) Lakes*, by Donald R. Whitehead, Donald F. Charles, Stephen T. Jackson, Susan E. Reed, and Mark C. Sheehan, 1986, chapter 18; and *Diatoms and Lake Acidity*, by Smol, J.P., Battarbee, R.W., Davis, R.B., and Merilainen, J. (eds.), 1986. (Dr. W. Junk Publishers, Dordrecht. ISBN 90-6193-536-9.)

4 For an informative recollection of the early logging period, see "Lumbering High on the High Peaks," by James A. Goodwin, in *Adirondac*, XLVI (7), pp. 3–5, September 1982.

5 For logging and forest fire occurrences, locations, and dates, see Fire Protection Map of the Adirondack Park, compiled by Karl Schmitt, forester, State of New York Conservation Commission, 1916.

6 See "Adirondack Insights #19: Fir Waves," *Adirondac* LII (5), pp. 19–21, June 1988.

7 See "Adirondack Insights #21: Geography of Adirondack Tree Species," *Adirondac* LIII (5), pp. 12–13, June 1989.

THE TREES

Identification Key To The Trees

The following key will help you to identify an unknown tree by means of step-by-step elimination of choices in a series of paired statements that contrast certain features of the trees in question. To identify a tree species, first examine your leaf and determine which of the first two alternatives (1:1) applies to your specimen. Proceed to the next pair of statements as directed by the key number at the end of the line following your choice (2:2, 15:15). Continue until the name of the species, instead of another number, appears at the right-hand margin. After you have arrived at a tentative identification, check it against the description and photographs—leaf and silhouette or bark—of the species in this guide.

1.	Leaves needle-like or scale-like: the conifers	2
1.	Leaves broad and flat: the hardwoods	15
2.	Leaves needle-like, many times longer than broad	3
2.	Leaves scale-like, nearly as broad as long	14
3.	Leaves borne several in a cluster	4
3.	Leaves borne singly along the stem	9
4.	Needles 15 or more per cluster	TAMARACK
4.	Needles 2 to 5 per cluster	5
5.	Needles slender, 5 per cluster	EASTERN WHITE PINE
5.	Needles stout, 2 or 3 per cluster	6

6.	Needles 3 per cluster	PITCH PINE
6.	Needles 2 per cluster	7
7.	Needles under 2 inches long, spread from the base in a V-shape	JACK PINE
7.	Needles over 2 inches long, lying close together along their length	8
8.	Needles 5 inches long, yellow-green	RED PINE
8.	Needles 3 inches long, blue-green	SCOTCH PINE
9.	Leaves flat	10
9.	Leaves four-sided	11
10.	Leaves ½ inch long, attached by a leaf stalk	EASTERN HEMLOCK
10.	Leaves 1 inch long, attached directly to the twig	BALSAM FIR
11.	Leaves dull yellow-green	12
11.	Leaves shiny blue-green	13
12.	Twigs smooth; leaves 1 inch long, essentially straight	NORWAY SPRUCE
12.	Twigs hairy; leaves ⅔ inch long, somewhat curved	RED SPRUCE
13.	Twigs smooth; leaves 1 inch long	WHITE SPRUCE
13.	Twigs hairy; leaves ½ inch long	BLACK SPRUCE
14.	Leafy twigs flat, forming sprays	NORTHERN WHITE-CEDAR
14.	Leafy twigs four-sided, not forming sprays	EASTERN REDCEDAR

15. Leaves compound, composed of several leaflets 16
15. Leaves all simple 18

16. Leaves arranged singly along the twig; leaflets 13 or more American Mountain-Ash
16. Leaves arranged in opposite pairs on the twig; leaflets 11 or fewer 17

17. Leaflets egg-shaped, smooth on the margin, generally 7, stalked White Ash
17. Leaflets oblong, toothed along the margin, generally 9, not stalked Black Ash

18. Leaves arranged in opposite pairs along the twig 19
18. Leaves arranged singly along the twig 21

19. Leaf margin smooth between the points of the lobes Sugar Maple
19. Leaf margin sharply toothed between the points 20

20. Leaves under 5 inches long, with short, acute lobes Red Maple
20. Leaves over 5 inches long, with long, tapered lobes Striped Maple

21. Leaves lobed Northern Red Oak
21. Leaves unlobed 22

22. Leaves unsymmetrical at base 23
22. Leaves symmetrical at base 24

23. Leaves elliptical in shape, widest near the middle, margin teeth irregular in size American Elm
23. Leaves broadly egg-shaped, widest near the base; margin teeth uniform in size American Basswood

24.	Leaf stalk flat	25
24.	Leaf stalk round	26
25.	Leaves under 2 inches long, with small teeth	QUAKING ASPEN
25.	Leaves over 2 inches long, with large teeth	BIGTOOTH ASPEN
26.	Orange fuzz present along main vein on lower surface	BLACK CHERRY
26.	Orange fuzz absent	27
27.	Leaves triangular in shape	GRAY BIRCH
27.	Leaves not triangular in shape	28
28.	Leaves whitish on under surface; margin with rounded teeth	BALSAM POPLAR
28.	Leaves light green on under surface; margin with pointed teeth	29
29.	Margin smooth except for tooth at end of each side vein	AMERICAN BEECH
29.	Margin continuously toothed	30
30.	Leaves narrowly tapered from the base	FIRE CHERRY
30.	Leaves rounded or elliptical	31
31.	Leaf margin with small, uniform teeth	SHADBUSH
31.	Leaf margin, with large, irregular teeth	32
32.	Leaf round or egg-shaped in outline	PAPER BIRCH
32.	Leaf elliptical in outline	33
33.	Leaves of thin texture; upper surface with scattered hairs; twigs not aromatic	EASTERN HOPHORNBEAM
33.	Leaves of thick texture; upper surface without scattered hairs, twigs aromatic	YELLOW BIRCH

Tree Species

The following catalog of trees includes only those native species found growing naturally on wild forest land in the high peak region or, in two cases, introduced conifers found in artificial plantations. Each description is accompanied by photos of a leaf and a silhouette (conifers) or bark (hardwoods). Also, key features are included for use with the silhouette and bark photos.

Conifer Silhouettes

It is often easier, with experience, to identify species of conifers by their general appearance and silhouette rather than by the close-up details of their foliage. Thus the conifer photographs are intended to convey that more subjective identification from a short distance away; the foliage details should be used to verify the identification.

Hardwood Bark

Although most hardwood species exhibit a similar branching habit with high spreading crowns and are difficult to distinguish by silhouette alone, the bark of most trees is sufficiently different to be recognized by the observant hiker. However, the bark does change as it becomes thicker with age, in many species sometimes dramatically so, thus complicating the identification. In the hardwood bark photographs we have tried to present the most typical form of each species as your most reasonable starting point in learning the variations of each. On larger trees, younger bark may still be seen on the larger limbs up in the crown. The white bar in each photo is a 6-inch ruler, for providing scale.

1. Eastern White Pine *Pinus strobus*

Eastern White Pine is the aristocrat among our conifers. Tallest of the native evergreens, it frequently attains 130-ft. heights and 4-ft. diameters. Open-grown trees, massive in appearance, support luxurious live branches nearly to the ground; forest-grown specimens, on the other hand, have small crowns topping long trunks of little taper and few side branches. In White Pine, side limbs come out horizontally in whorls of 4 or 5 at successive levels up the trunk, each whorl indicating a year's growth. In contrast to all other conifers of the region, White Pine remains vigorous and fast-growing for 150 to 250 years, accounting for reports of trees over 150 feet tall in pre-settlement forests. Today in our second-growth forests it is rare to see a tree over two-thirds that size anywhere in the state.

White Pine today is an important species throughout the Adirondack forests, far more abundant than in pre-settlement times. For many decades it has been a common invader of old fields abandoned from unprofitable farming along the eastern side of the Adirondacks, where soils are too sandy and infertile for sustained agriculture. Elsewhere, trees occur either in pure stands or, more commonly, in mixtures with other species following severe disturbances. Rated as intermediate in tolerance, White Pine holds its own against invasion by hardwoods on less-fertile sandy sites, which tend to be droughty, but it is eventually replaced by more tolerant hardwoods on better upland sites. Because of its great ecological aggressiveness, however, White Pine typically acts as a

Eastern White Pine. The foliage of Eastern White Pine is clustered on branches along the upper side of large horizontal limbs. Further, Eastern White Pine trees consistently outgrow their arboreal associates, and thus the tops of their crowns typically emerge above the forest canopy.

pioneer species following blowdown or other drastic forest disturbance, whence its designation by foresters as a "catastrophe species." Seedlings of White Pine quickly establish dominance over their associates because they are the fastest-growing conifer in the Northeast and also because they send down a deep tap root, which grows a foot or more in length annually for several years following germination—far deeper than roots of any other conifer or most hardwoods.

Although a favored plantation species for many years, White Pine is now planted less often because of severe damage caused by White-Pine blister rust and by the White-Pine weevil. In addition, dead limbs remain on the trunks of plantation-grown White Pine for many decades, thereby causing loose knots in the lumber. Old-growth, clear pine lumber from large trees, however, is soft, even-grained, and easily worked, thus being a desirable species for general utility purposes. Given full sunlight, White Pine with its plume-like branches makes an excellent ornamental, as numerous planted trees attest.

White Pine is one of the easiest conifers to recognize. All the pines have needles clustered together in tight bundles distributed closely along the twig, but only in White Pine are the needles in fives. The individual needles are slender, bluish green, 3 to 5 inches long, and tend to spread apart from the base of the cluster. Because the needles persist on the trees for only two years, the needles seem to be confined to the outer ends of the twigs, and the older portion of the slender branch appears bare of foliage.

White Pine may be identified also by either the bark or the cones. Until the trunk is about 6 or 8 inches in diameter the bark remains quite smooth and of a greenish-black color, but thereafter it breaks up into elongated blocks minutely scaly on the surface and separated by deep fissures. The cones, which may be found around the base of the tree in the spring, average 5 inches long and an inch or two wide, with about 40 relatively flat scales. Fresh cones collected directly from the tree in late summer or fall are green to light brown and often have yellowish globs of dried pitch on the tips of some of the scales. White Pine is widely scattered throughout low elevations in the high peak region, though rarely going up the slopes higher than 2,500 feet. It is especially common around lake shores elsewhere in the park, in which cases it often shows the typical flagging of wind-stressed trees. Individual large trees may be found as "culls" left by the loggers because of some type of defect or rot in the trunk. Any large old stump you find in the woods over 2 feet in diameter is likely the remains of a White Pine. Similarly, if you see a conifer from a distance sticking up above the forest canopy, it too is likely a White Pine outgrowing its associates.

Key: long horizontal limbs, gently upturned, with masses of foliage on the upper side; often appearing windswept (called "flagging") when growing exposed to the prevailing winds.

2. Red Pine *Pinus resinosa*

Red Pine is as attractive and valuable a tree as White Pine, perhaps more so, but it has not maintained itself in the face of the heavy logging of yesteryear. The trees do not withstand competition well, and the species is accordingly rated as intolerant. Red Pine requires a light, sandy, well-aerated soil to grow vigorously; on any other soil type other species will soon shade it out. In the original forests Red Pine was much less common than White Pine, and many of the trees we see now are plantations put in since the 1930s when the Civilian Conservation Corps and the

Red Pine. The long, dark leaves of Red Pine are closely packed at the ends of the upper limbs, and thereby produce a dense and dome-like crown; the shaded lower branches soon loose their needles and are in turn shed, particularly where crowded trees form a continuous canopy cover.

Conservation Department began to use Red Pine, a fairly pest-free species, in place of White. In plantations, Red Pine slows down in growth rate after 50 to 60 years; accordingly, trees rarely reach heights over 70 or 80 feet. When found in natural conditions, Red Pine typically occurs in pure stands, as few other species can survive the extremely dry soils on which it thrives.

Red Pine has a heavier foliage than any other native conifer in our region. The paired needles are 5–6 inches long, fairly stout, deep yellow-green, and persist on the tree for four or five years, giving the limbs a bushy appearance denser than that of other evergreens. Open-grown trees develop a symmetrical, oval crown and are considered among our most beautiful ornamentals. The young trunks quickly become scaly with a pale orangish-brown cast; in age the bark breaks up into irregular plates resembling alligator hide. The cones are shaped like a large egg, chestnut-brown in color; the scales, though flat as in White Pine, are thickened on the top side near the outer end of the scale.

In the high peak region most of the commercially valuable Red Pine was logged off years ago, but scattered stands may still be seen. A striking stand of natural Red Pine silhouettes the rocky ridge to your right as you go up the ski lift on Whiteface Mountain; you cross through this stand when hiking on the Wilmington–Whiteface trail. A small stand is encountered on the trail to The Brothers from Keene Valley. Numerous plantations of Red Pine now also dot the highway landscape in the high peak region. Mixed stands of Red and White Pine and other conifers line most of the stony shoreline and bluffs surrounding the St. Regis Canoe Area. Lovely specimens planted for the Lake Placid Club by Orville Cobane in the early '30s form part of the tree cover around the campgrounds and Loj area at Heart Lake.

Key: dense clusters of fairly long leaves clustered at end of branches, the rest of the symmetrical canopy appearing relatively open.

3. Jack Pine *Pinus banksiana*

In an ecological sense Jack Pine is one of our most interesting trees. It is, first of all, a cold-climate Canadian species with only scattered southern outliers in New York and New England; it is thus a species of the sub-Arctic spruce-fir forests rather than the warm temperate-zone lands where most American pines are found. Moreover, the tree thrives on barren ground, shallow soils over bedrock, rocky knobs, and deep sands—soils on which few trees can gain a permanent foothold. The trees are small in stature, sometimes contorted in form, but they are nonetheless hardy on impoverished soils where few other species survive. What is most curious about this species is the way it prospers despite wildfire. The trees start producing cones when only a few years old; these persist attached to the branch for many years, many of them remaining closed and not releasing their seeds. In time, a wildfire sweeping through the forest will char and dry out the closed cones; with competing vegetation destroyed and needed mineral soil exposed, the cones slowly open and literally millions of viable seeds sift to the ground, there quickly forming a dense new stand of Jack Pine. In the biological world, a time of crisis may be the opportunity of a lifetime!

Once you see a Jack Pine you'll not easily forget it: it looks as much like a limby larch as a pine; this is because the needles are only an inch or two long, far shorter than in other American pines. Also unique, the two leaves in the bundle diverge from the base at an acute angle, forming a "V" pattern. When in doubt, look for the cones, which in this species always seem to be present; they are

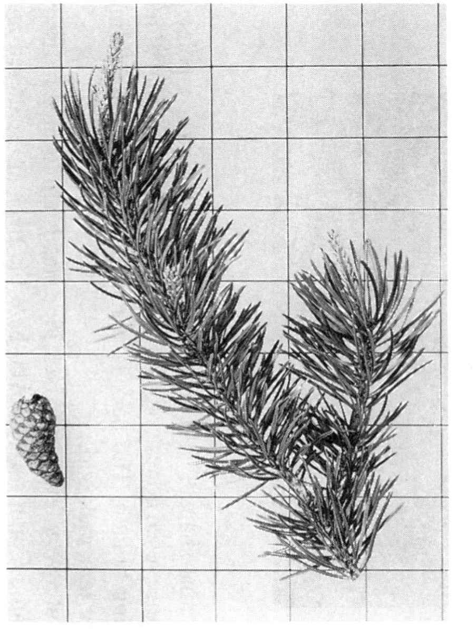

Jack Pine. Jack Pine rarely produces large side limbs, rather the foliage of short, stout needles is borne on short side branches arising from the main trunk, thereby creating a narrow silhouette of thin trees, which condition in turn produces dense stands of trees growing close to each other.

indeed "cone-shaped," like an ice-cream cone. The narrow pointed ends of the closed cones point forward toward the outer end of the supporting branch. The bark is blackish and scaly, resembling spruce or tamarack bark.

All but a very few of our Jack Pine stands are located in Essex and Clinton Counties, and even here the trees are scattered and infrequent. In our area the closest trees are found along Hardy Road in the town of Wilmington, and north and east of Jay. A few trees survive at 1500 feet on the north spur of Poke-O-Moonshine Mountain. There is a considerable stand on the southwest end of the Jay Range. To see a continuous forest stand of (stunted) Jack Pine, venture north to the "Flat Rock" near Altona in Clinton County.

Key: dense, compact canopy of short needles, deep green, the branches bearing annual clusters of persistent, conical cones, all pointing outward toward end of branch, many remaining closed several years.

4. Pitch Pine *Pinus rigida*

In many ways Pitch Pine is a southern counterpart to Jack Pine. It too grows on the driest, most unproductive of sandy sites. It too is a relatively small tree generally too scraggly to be economically important. And it also is favored by fire, at least light fires that consume competing hardwoods and brush. In contrast to other conifers, young Pitch Pines sprout from the ground level when their tops are killed, as by fire, or if their trunks are cut down. Similarly, if a flash crown fire burns the foliage but does not damage the internal tissues within the trunk, new needles sprout green from dormant buds hidden beneath the fire-blackened bark. The only significant ecological difference between Jack Pine and Pitch Pine is the marked preference of the latter for warmer climes, as on Long Island, where it is a dominant species over many miles of dunes.

Pitch Pine is easily recognized by foliage, being our only species that has needles borne consistently in threes. The leaves, about 3 inches long, are relatively sparse on the branch, so the crown appears very open; this feature, with the pale yellow-green of the foliage, makes Pitch Pine an easy species to recognize from afar. In addition, the cones, though generally releasing their seeds on schedule, persist for years attached in clusters of two to four along the main limbs; occasionally these cones become partially engulfed by wood as the branches grow outward. Individual cones resemble those of Red Pine, but the swollen portion at the end of each scale is tipped with a sharp point.

Pitch Pine barely extends into the high peak region. It is frequently encountered south of Lake George and again northeastward in the Ausable Forks–Clintonville area, where several local roads pass through pure stands of Pitch Pine. Pitch Pine is the most abundant tree species in McComb Reservation State Park at the northeastern corner of the Adirondack State Park.

Key: sparse canopy of yellow-green needles; open, spherical cones may be persistent; bark becoming blocky in age; trunk often openly branched in crown.

Pitch Pine. The foliage of Pitch Pine is intermediate in length between Jack and Red Pines, but the trees are irregularly limbed and branched, which in turn creates an unsymmetrical canopy. As with Jack Pine, persistent cones may be seen in silhouette against the sky.

5. Scotch Pine *Pinus sylvestris*

One more pine will be seen by the hiker—Scotch Pine, or Scots Pine, the most widely distributed tree in the world. This European species was first brought to our shores late in the nineteenth century, when the budding profession of forestry needed a tried and proved species with which to reforest lands devastated by the intensive logging and wildfires of the day. Scotch Pine was such a species, and seed was readily available from foreign suppliers. Most of our oldest conifer plantations are thus of an exotic species not native to this continent; but then so are we! And like us, Scotch Pine has become naturalized, reproducing its kind around the original plantings. With time it is being assimilated into the local wild populations, to grow and prosper on its own strengths and abilities. Indeed, the "Americanization" of Scotch Pine is now so complete it has become the leading Christmas tree species in New York State.

The success story of Scotch Pine is marred by one failing: across its natural range the species varies greatly in trunk form and branching habit, and not all the stock from which we got our seed was of high quality. This accounts in good measure for the crooked trunks seen in older plantations. With greater care in the selection of seed, the problem is being brought under control. Meanwhile, the forester likes Scotch Pine because it will grow anywhere; so will Jack Pine, of course, but Scotch Pine by contrast continues to grow vigorously to sawlog sizes—that is, to diameters over a foot. Farmers have found Scotch Pine an excellent species for growing on impoverished fields withdrawn from cultivation.

Scotch Pine. Both foliage and form are highly variable in Scotch Pine, given the different origin of their seed sources in Europe; any version of green and any tree shape may be expected. Open-grown trees, in particular, may be contorted and crooked due to local site conditions, especially snow damage.

Scotch Pine is immediately recognizable by its orange bark. Even on large trees where the bark has become dark and furrowed, the younger trunk and branches higher up in the crown are orange. The leaves, 2–3 inches long and in pairs, are bluish green and typically have a faint silvery sheen. The cones tend to point backward toward the base of the branch, just the opposite of the direction in Jack Pine; moreover, the cones are smaller than in Red Pine, tawny or yellow brown in color, and knobby or warty at the end of each scale.

One has no trouble finding Scotch Pine in the non-mountainous portions of the Adirondacks; it is common as both scattered ornaments and plantation trees. Years ago the state planted thousands of Scotch Pine and Red Pine all along the South Meadows Road; the camping area at the Meadows is practically pure Scotch Pine. Because it is such an aggressive pioneering species, it is now characteristic of much of the abandoned farmland in the tri-lakes region.

Key: young trunk orangish, turning brown in age; foliage distinctly bluish; trunks often contorted and with broken branches due to ice storms.

6. Tamarack *Larix laricina*

Our native Eastern Larch, better known locally as Tamarack, has the distinction of being the only northern conifer that sheds its needles completely each fall; all other conifers are evergreen, dropping only a third or quarter of their foliage in any one year.

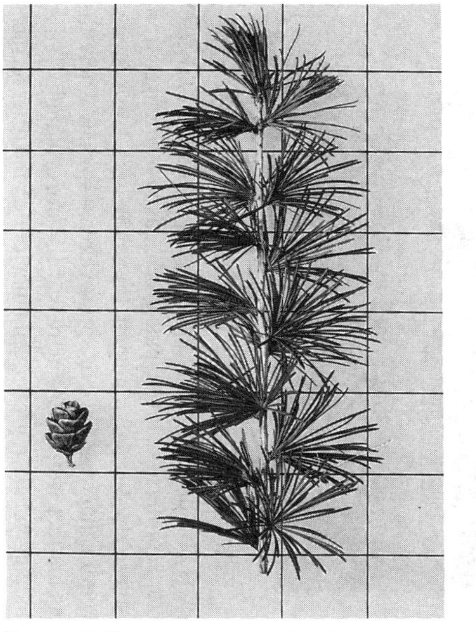

Tamarack. Tamarack, our only deciduous "evergreen" species, is in fact one of the conifers, as the small cones borne erect along the twigs will show any time of the year, but in winter it resembles a swamp—inhabiting hardwood—whereas in summer it exhibits typical conifer foliage.

Tamarack is also distinct in having the lightest-colored foliage of northeastern conifers—a lovely pale green, easily recognized from great distance. In our area one gets the impression larch is confined to cool sphagnum bogs or springy areas—places where the hiker gets his feet wet. This is only half the story, though; Tamarack will do even better, grow even taller, out on the drier terraces and flats away from the bog—on sandy soils, for example, rather than peat. But Tamarack is so intolerant of shade that on those better sites the other species crowd it out. Tamarack is by far our most sensitive conifer: either it finds a site where it can grow as a dominant tree, free of competition, or it quickly dies out. Its abundance on saturated soils, such as floating mats around bogs, is due solely to the fact that here the site is too unfavorable for growth of most other trees. Tamarack is one of the very few that can withstand the roots' being completely and permanently submerged.

Another foliage feature of larch sets it off clearly from associates: the side twigs along the main branches do not elongate each year, so the leaves are clumped together on stubby spur shoots generally not more than ½ inch long. The effect of the slender, delicate leaves, hardly over an inch long, is very lacy and feminine. On the branch one sees an abundance of cones, each less than an inch long and borne erect by virtue of an upward twist of the supporting stalk. Growing in forest conditions where trees are 50–60 feet tall, the oblong silhouette is quite characteristic: a straight trunk right to the top of the crown and all the side branches very short and of about the same length.

Tamarack is much more common (and taller) in the hill and lake country of the western Adirondacks than in the high peak region. Only scattered trees will be found on the mountain slopes (such as the ones on the sides of the slides on the north face of Colden); an occasional specimen will even be seen in the alpine meadow of ten of our alpine peaks. Typically, the species is confined to drainages, wet bogs, or meadows. A number of trees can be seen at South Meadows, a typical habitat for the species.

Key: sparse, pale, blue-green foliage; most open crown of any conifer; leaves deciduous.

7. Eastern Hemlock *Tsuga canadensis*

Eastern Hemlock played an important role in the early logging history of New York State: trees were felled for the tannin-rich bark, and the stripped trunks were then abandoned in the woods. Hemlock lumber was widely disdained because the wood is coarse-grained and splintery; loggers despised it because the knots are hard enough to blunt an ax. On the other hand, Hemlock was heavily harvested elsewhere in the Adirondacks for its bark, from which tannin was extracted for producing leather. (See *Hides, Hemlock and Adirondack History* by Barbara McMartin.) In any case, hemlock has been so selectively logged and eliminated that most of us have lost appreciation of its former abundance. A visit to one of our few remaining virgin stands will give you a better measure of its importance under natural forest conditions.

The feature that saved hemlock from complete extirpation under heavy logging pressures was its tolerance: it is the most tolerant conifer in the East. Tolerant of shade, young trees too small for the logger can survive long years, growing ever so slowly, under the densest canopy in the forest. The tree will hold on for decades until some disturbance in the forest makes an opening into which the crown will quickly grow. "Tenacious" is the word for hemlock, ecologically speaking.

Hemlock differs from many of our Adirondack conifers in one

Eastern Hemlock. Eastern Hemlock may be recognized by the weeping aspect of the foliage wherein the smaller branches and twigs droop downward at an angle. The shade-tolerant foliage persists on the lower branches until the canopy fully closes above.

particular habitat characteristic: it is less of a "northern" species than spruce and fir, and it grows just as well among hardwoods, which is to say it does best under somewhat milder climates—cool-moist conditions rather than cold-moist. The healthiest trees are found where the soil is constantly damp and the atmospheric humidity high—along streams, in wooded glens, on north-facing slopes, and near the borders of lakes and ponds.

One other characteristic should be noted. Most conifers require mineral soil to become established. Hemlock, however, reproduces very well on mossy logs, where, incidentally, it often competes with Yellow Birch. The next time you see a group of young hemlock saplings, check to see if they are aligned in a row; if so, kick the soil between the trees and you will likely see the decaying trunk of an old fallen tree.

Most people come to recognize hemlock by its color and form: color, because it is the most somber blue-green of any conifer in our woods; form, because the delicate and slender "leaders," or branch tips, droop downward toward the ground. Up close you will see that each leaf is supported on the twig by a slender petiole or stalk—a feature typical of hardwoods, of course, but most unusual for a conifer. The leaves have two white bands running lengthwise on the under surface; also, most of the leaves are arranged in two rows, one on either side of the twig, thus giving each spray a flat appearance. The cones resemble those of Tamarack but are pendulous. If a striking cut is made into the bark with a knife, purplish streaks or layers will be seen inside.

Hemlock is rare to infrequent on the cut-over mountainsides now in the high peak region, though fairly frequent or common elsewhere on more level ground. I know of only a single tree on the entire Algonquin trail. The hiker sees it in the occasional pockets of virgin growth that escaped the fires and the loggers, such as on the lower slopes of the Adirondack Mountain Reserve lands at the Ausable Club; beautiful old trees line the West Side Trail, for example. Climbing Giant via Roaring Brook, you pass through a nearly pure stand of old-growth hemlock at about 0.75 miles, just before the trail crosses the brook to the south side of the drainage. These trees have been studied by scientists and found to be four hundred years old, the oldest ones in the high peaks. Such stands, of course, typified portions of the old-growth condition on mountainsides in late glacial times, we believe, before the hemlock decline some four thousand years ago, long before Red Spruce arrived in the region and took over that dominant role.

Key: dark green foliage in delicate flat sprays; tips of side branches drooping.

8. Red Spruce *Picea rubens*

A whole book could be written about the biology of Red Spruce in the Adirondacks. In a very real sense it is *the* Adirondack conifer, the one species most typical of the region as a whole. Early records convince me that Red Spruce characteristically constituted a minimum of 25 percent of the forest cover in the northern Adirondacks. Like White Pine, Adirondack Red Spruce has been hard-hit by the ax and saw for over a hundred and sixty years; but when left alone, as in the Forest Preserve today, the tree recovers from that onslaught better than its associates and in time regains its former eminence.

The reasons for this regional success are several. First of all, Red Spruce is very high on the scale of tolerance. Only hemlock is higher (and in this case only by a small amount). But Red Spruce is climatically adapted to the colder mountain environments, while hemlock is slightly north of its optimum climate. Secondly, Red Spruce will withstand suppression for upward of a hundred years without succumbing; it will grow in the shade, barely holding on, for decades, then explode back to a fast growth rate as soon as the canopy opens up because of some local disturbance. During all this time it maintains its "apical dominance": it keeps just one top leader slowly pushing upward—it does not start to bush out in all directions, as many species do in the shade. Being a long-lived species, it can spend 150 years or more slowly gaining a canopy position, and then live another two hundred years as a dominant, all the while casting its seed into whatever new openings may appear. Finally, in primeval forests Red Spruce had few natural enemies in the fungus and insect worlds to contend with. The larger animals have no particular use for it; the deer won't eat its sharp needles even as a starvation food. Red Spruce is as suited to the Adirondacks as any tree species could conceivably be.

The wild spruce you see on Adirondack uplands will in all probability be Red. White Spruce is on level ground and is quite rare here, and Black Spruce is confined to boggy lowlands and, rarely, open summits. Red Spruce trees may be recognized by the deep yellow-green of their foliage—no bluish cast whatsoever. With

Red Spruce. Most of the foliage of Red Spruce is borne on short side branches off the main limbs, thus giving a slender outline to each limb. The color aspect of the foliage is dark or dull green.

practice one will learn to pick trees out by their characteristic silhouette, but that skill comes with experience.

As with all spruces, the leaves of Red Spruce are four-sided and borne on short pegs along the orangish brown twigs. The needles are ⅔ of an inch long. If growing in the sun, they arch up toward the top of the twig and are somewhat blunt; otherwise, when shaded, they stand out straight in all directions, quite sharp to the touch. The cones have an ovoid shape, about 1½ inches long; in color they vary from reddish at first to chestnut-brown at maturity. The bark is dark and scaly. Dried resin secreted from wounds along the trunk was once the source of "spruce gum."

Red Spruce is always around us in the high peak region. Mature trees, now seen only in isolated virgin stands, average 80 feet in height and somewhat over 2 feet in diameter. Upward on the slopes the trees become progressively shorter; near 4000 feet, where they gradually give way to pure fir forests, the trees may be only 40 feet tall, often less, although advanced in age.

Unfortunately, most of the Red Spruce we see in the high country today is in a decline that began in the early 1960s and is only now becoming stabilized. The canopy trees particularly have lost much of their foliage and are in a slow decline, if not already dead. As you go up Phelps Brook from Marcy Dam on your way to Mt. Marcy, for example, look up to your right at the virgin forest high above: you'll see that essentially every Red Spruce in the canopy has lost part of its crown. You have to fly over the region and look down on the dead tops to appreciate the full impact of the decline throughout the region. For the past five years, however, the situation has improved markedly. Few surviving trees show further over-winter needle browning or needle loss; hopefully, the tighter pollution controls now in effect may allow the survivors to recover. In the fall of 1994, a good seed year, even declining trees bore a heavy cone crop.

Key: crown broadly conical, medium green; main side branches with gentle upward arch; cones sparse on ends of upper branches.

9. Black Spruce *Picea mariana*

To most observers Black Spruce is not so exciting or important a species as Red, but it is equally distinctive. The ecology of Black Spruce can be best understood by realizing that it only occurs where it can get its roots into saturated soils, either boggy mucks or wet sands. Across the Adirondacks we see both Red and Black Spruce growing in such habitats, but whereas Red Spruce grows near water that is moving and fresh, Black Spruce is most abundant where the water is stagnant, as in a closed bog with no outlet. This is the same habitat, you will recall, that Tamarack favors; in fact, these two species are common associates throughout their range in North America.

These boggy sites, where few other species can survive, offer the least productive growing conditions anywhere in the state. If you kept accurate track of the growth rate of such Black Spruces, you would see that they often need 30 years to grow an inch in diameter. Curiously, the larger trees well back from the center of a bog are generally no older than the shorter ones near the water's edge.

Conifers typically do not reproduce vegetatively as do the hardwoods. Pitch Pine is one exception, and Black Spruce is the other—but of a different type. The latter's branches sweep down and then bend up, and when growing in a bog they may come into contact with the sphagnum moss covering the ground. Because sphagnum generally grows upward about half an inch a year, the middle portion of the branch may become engulfed by the moss; when this happens, it may sprout roots and shortly become an independent plant, much as a gardener may root a cutting. Upward of a dozen "offspring" may thus surround a parent tree. In rare cases, as on the Plains of the Oswegatchie, south of Cranberry Lake, three generations of trees so evolved may form concentric rings, each successive ring outward being shorter and of course younger. This process, called "layering," is the source of over half the natural reproduction of Black Spruce in the muskeg country of northwestern Canada.

The distribution of Black Spruce in the high peak region is unlike that of any other tree species. We have little low-elevation boggy country suitable for this spruce. But Black Spruce—hold on to your hat!—grows on many of our summits. Here, where sphagnum moss is an important component of the alpine tundra, so is the Black Spruce. The severe environment seems to force the tree to assume a dwarfed, shrubby form, but Black Spruce it still is. Around the timberline, as on Wright Peak (for one conspicuous example), the branches typically spread out laterally for many feet, though the "trees" are only two feet high. In the windswept alpine zone, Black Spruce may be only one to two feet tall but 30 years old. Being fairly tolerant, a few survive a short distance downslope

Black Spruce. The foliage of Black Spruce is densely clustered on the short side branches, giving trees a narrow oblong silhouette. The reflected light is slightly shiny and bluish. Trees growing in acid bogs are often stunted and malformed, reflective of their poor growth on such difficult sites.

in the balsam, but these soon are over-topped and die.

Black Spruce is generally not difficult to recognize. The leaves are the shortest among the spruces, only ½ inch long. They are silvery blue-green, unlike the dull yellow-green of Red Spruce. The persistent and purple cones, rarely seen on the alpine trees but evident on the bog ones, are smaller than on Red Spruce, perfectly spherical in shape, and persist on the trees for several years. As the branches grow outward, the cones appear to have been borne in the middle of the crown.

The largest Black Spruce I have seen on the mountains is about 12 feet tall and 6 inches in diameter, just a few feet below the open summit ridge on the trail up Mt. Colden from Lake Arnold. Typical but small Black Spruce occur on the summit of Mt. Jo. A few scattered trees will be seen at South Meadows. To see dense, continuous stands of Black Spruce, drive the Oregon Plains road north out of Bloomingdale or west toward Gabriels and you'll see Black Spruce–dominated countryside resembling northern Canada.

Key: crown oblong, compact, of short side branches, bluish green; cones purplish, clustered around main trunk at top of tree.

10. White Spruce *Picea glauca*

Across the transcontinental coniferous forest of Canada, Tamarack and Black and White Spruce constitute the dominant climax cover. All three continue northward to the arctic tree line, though at those high latitudes they resemble shrubs more than forest trees.

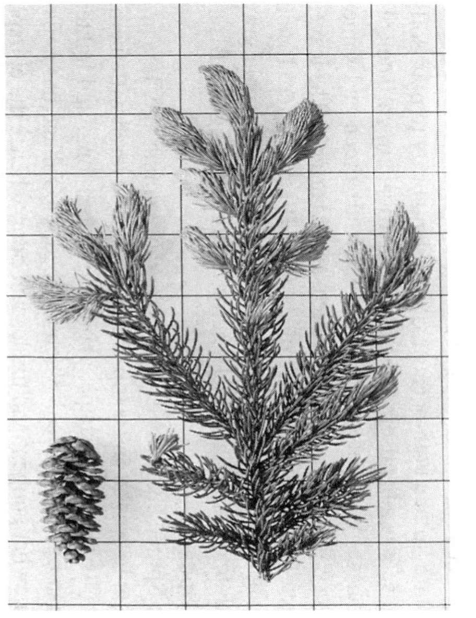

White Spruce. White Spruce becomes a massive and heavily branched tree with a columnar outline when growing in the open, with more densely arranged but lighter-colored foliage than in Red Spruce; in the fall and winter clustered cones often give a brownish cast to the upper canopy.

Southward, Tamarack and Black Spruce extend into Pennsylvania, but White Spruce drops out in the Adirondacks. This quicker drop-out of White Spruce is curious in view of the fact that of all seven native American spruces, White grows best when planted experimentally in the southern states. Within its range, White Spruce typically occupies the river banks, lake shores, and moist slopes, yet south of its natural range it does well on dry sites: it has proved to be a good species for reclaiming spoil banks left in the wake of strip mining in Pennsylvania and Ohio—perhaps the severest test we can expect of a planted tree.

Because of its general hardiness on adverse sites, foresters have long experimented with White Spruce as a plantation species. As seedlings and saplings, White Spruce will grow faster than most evergreens except pines and will take care of itself when first set into the ground. In recent years landscape architects have begun to use White Spruce both because of its adaptability to poor soils and because it is a handsome tree of symmetrical crown. The coloration basically is that of Black Spruce: blue-green and somewhat silvery, though this latter feature is quite variable. The leaves are an inch long, twice the size of those in Black Spruce. If you have a magnifying glass, look at the twigs: they are a pale gray color and smooth, not minutely hairy as are the twigs of Black and Red Spruce.

White Spruce bears cones at a remarkably young age. It is not uncommon to see the entire top of a 10-ft. tree covered with them. Each cone is oblong in shape, about 1½ inches long, and lighter brown than on Red Spruce. When crushed, the foliage has a distinct, somewhat pungent and unpleasant odor, whence the epitaph

"Cat Spruce" among some woods workers. Try it. If you own a cat, you'll understand.

Don't look for White Spruce on the mountains when hiking—it isn't there, because it requires richer soil. In the northern Adirondacks, its natural southern range limit, it is found in scattered stands only in a few valleys surrounding the high peak region, such as along the Blue Ridge road westward toward Newcomb. On the northern side it is quite common along the Ausable River from the Olympic Ski Jump complex northward along the Riverside Road over four miles to the Wilmington Road. Many natural ornamental trees are seen around Lake Placid, Saranac Lake, and the former farmlands around Franklin Falls and Bloomingdale, where richer soils prevail.

Key: resembling Red Spruce in form but with denser foliage at ends of side branches, which may be up-turned; foliage distinctly bluish green; cones abundant at ends of upper branches, semi-persistent through winter.

11. Norway Spruce *Picea abies*

Norway Spruce, of course, is not a native American species. Rather, it was the second exotic species of demonstrated worth (the first was Scotch Pine) imported at the time of our silvicultural crisis earlier in the century. The trees are vigorous and fast-growing in youth and thus easily established, but they are not suitable on our less fertile glacial soils. Ecologically, this tree is more demanding

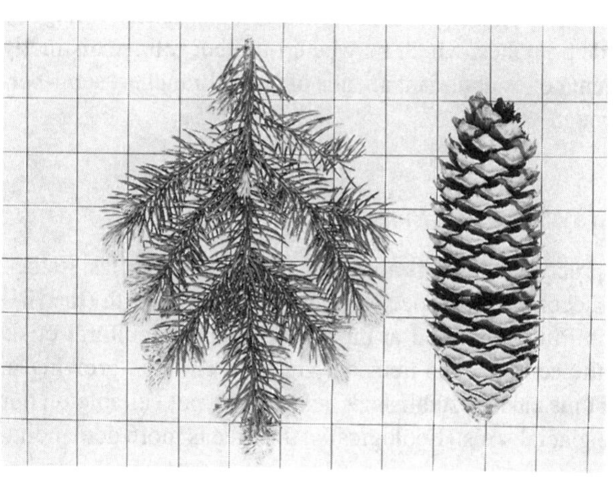

Norway Spruce. Norway Spruce is everywhere recognized when present by the pendent side branches dropping of the main limbs and, in the fall and winter, by the very large cones over 6" in length. Roadside plantings line much of the last mile of the ADK Loj Road.

than the native species; it must have a fertile site to maintain its growth rate. Because of its larger size, Norway Spruce has been preferred where the management objective has been sawlog trees as well as pulp sticks.

For many years this spruce was one of the major species distributed by the Conservation Department from the state tree nurseries. Unfortunately it is quite susceptible to the white-pine weevil, as much so as White Pine itself. Thousands of plantation-grown Norway Spruce in New York State are now usable only for pulp; the main trunk when weeviled in the lower 16 to 18 feet becomes too crooked for use as a sawlog. Meanwhile, Norway Spruce is such a beautiful tree that the horticulturists have picked it up as a major ornamental species. Norway Spruce in many ways resembles our native Red Spruce. It has the same coloration and a similar form, differing only in that the branchlets droop more and are not as crowded on the main horizontal limbs. Three specific points will distinguish the two: the cones of Norway Spruce are enormous for a spruce, 6–8 inches long; the leaves are half again or twice as long, averaging an inch in length; and the twigs lack the hair seen on Red Spruce.

Because Norway Spruce will be seen only as a planted species, artificially established, it should be easy to separate from our wild Red Spruce. On the other hand, years ago the state planted both Norway Spruce and Scotch Pine along most of the South Meadows Road and back on the Loj Road toward Highway 73. You pass by or under the drooping side branches of the Norway Spruce every time you drive into the Loj, and until recently, several ornamental Norway Spruces formed the canopy of trees over which you gazed toward the Great Range when relaxing on the veranda at Johns Brook Lodge.

Key: main branches arching upward, with side branches distinctly drooping; cones prominent near ends of main branches.

12. Balsam Fir *Abies balsamea*

We saw earlier that Red Spruce was the one species most representative of the Adirondack region as a whole. With equal justification Balsam Fir may be considered the species typical of the Adirondack high country where post-glacial organic soils cover the bedrock. In the natural, unlogged, unburned forests of the high peak region, Red Spruce and Balsam Fir shared dominance: the former was more abundant than the latter in the low levels of the spruce-fir belt, from about 2000 to 4000 feet, but balsam took over in pure stands for the last several hundred feet. The proof of this greater vigor and abundance of the balsam on the high slopes is apparent to those who climb the mountains in late spring: balsam buds start to open in mid-May, Red Spruce in mid-June, by which time the new balsam twigs are already 4 inches long. This greater aggressiveness of balsam is also obvious at lower elevations where the forest has been logged. Here balsam has returned quicker and more vigorously than the Red Spruce, though experience elsewhere shows that in a generation or two the slower-growing but slightly more tolerant Red Spruce will regain its co-dominant position.

The marvelous adaptation of Balsam Fir to the high mountain slopes is most striking in those areas where the great storm of November 25, 1950, leveled thousands of acres of forest cover. In most of the blowdown the balsam quickly seeded in, grew vigorously, and now controls the community with trees upward of 20 feet in height—vegetational recovery at its best, without loss of soil by erosion during the process. The ecological strength of

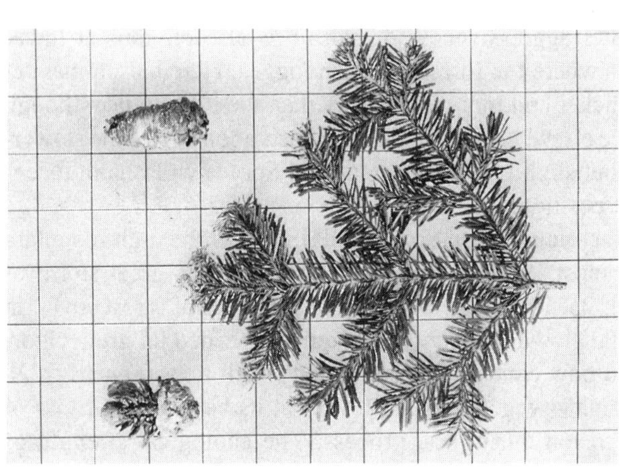

Balsam Fir. Balsam Fir is easily recognized from a short distance by the symmetrical spire-like crown resembling a church steeple. In good seed years, masses of erect, purple cones crowd the summit of the crown. On young trees, the gray bark with resin blisters verifies the identification.

Dendrology - The study
the department of botany
trees of trees.

Dendrologist - one versed in Dendrology,
a professed student of trees.

He or she use a dendrometer - an
instrument for measuring trees.

Commander Woodward Knight Dendrology.

this tree is demonstrated again at timberline: here the trees are very short, as is to be expected, but even when they finally give way to the alpine meadow they remain erect and tree-like, not prostrate and spreading as the occasional spruce will be. Moreover, they flower and fruit up here as prolifically as down below. Every climber has had the experience of pausing on the trail just short of the summit and turning to look out at the vista, only to find himself staring directly into a cluster of balsam cones on the top of a dwarfed fir head-high in front of him.

Balsam Fir is a common understory associate of Red Spruce along the drainages and flats in the lower country as well. This constant competition between spruce and balsam is one of the interesting, and continuing, ecological battles of the Adirondack forests. Balsam Fir is more vigorous in getting established after forest disturbance, but it is a short-lived species that cannot maintain its hold on the site. Red Spruce is slower in gaining a canopy position, but once there lives much longer, over-topping and suppressing the balsam.

Balsam Fir must be numbered among the most beautiful of all American conifers. It has a more symmetrical, spire-like crown than any other eastern species, and, with its silvery blue-green needles, perhaps the most beautiful foliage. Even the aroma of this species is a distinctive delight, the fragrance pleasing to the most inexperienced of climbers.

Those to whom balsam is new can recognize it by the narrow, flat leaves, about 1 inch long, borne on the twigs without stalks. The upper surface is dark blue-green, but the lower has two white lines from tip to base, as in hemlock. The leaves curve upward when growing in the sun, and lie flat when developed in the shade. The buds are distinctive too: three at the end of the twig, each round or barrel-shaped and covered with a reddish resin. The bark remains smooth throughout life except for an abundance of resin blisters all over the surface.

Everyone has his favorite species of tree, but I suspect more climbers have "adopted" this species than any other. It is *the* tree of the high country, providing a distinctive sensual experience to every climb. You experience the balsam aroma with every breath you take, and it somehow gets into your blood and consciousness, renewing its presence and pleasure whenever you just think "high country."

Key: crown narrowly symmetrical to base, compact, dark bluish green; purple, erect cones densely clustered at top of crown.

13. Northern White-cedar *Thuja occidentalis*

No one would know it simply by looking at the trees, but Northern White-cedar across its range acts like two different species; it consists of two ecological races distinct from each other in a functional way but outwardly identical. South of the Adirondacks, where soils are derived from limestone strata immediately beneath the surface and are therefore calcareous, one race of dry-site, lime-loving white-cedar will be found. But here in the high peak region, where over 95 percent of the soils are slightly to strongly acidic, a wet-site, acid-loving race is found. The two differ out-

Northern White-cedar. The flat sprays of dense foliage compactly arranged on short branches in Northern White-cedar make the trees appear very symmetrical in outline. Most trees are ovate in shape throughout their life. Foliage sprays are quite pungent when crushed.

wardly in no noticeable manner. The Adirondack trees, however, inhabit peaty bogs, or follow streams upslope, or occur around lake shores, as at Heart Lake, Lake Colden, and Elk Lake. Surprisingly, the species seems to have no altitudinal limit. It follows MacIntyre Brook up into the spruce-fir on Wright Peak, and a few dwarfed specimens survive there even above timberline.

The natural history of white-cedar in the Adirondacks is closely tied to that of the white-tailed deer. White-cedar is *the* favorite browse of the deer, and where the deer are abundant, the White-cedar is reduced to minimal numbers. The same threat holds for hemlock, only slightly lower on the deer scale of preference. Because it is one of our slowest growing conifers, white-cedar is especially susceptible to damage from deer browsing in the low-elevation forests of the Adirondacks. It is not seriously affected here in the high peak region.

White-cedar is so different in leaf structure from the other conifers of the high peak region that one has little trouble in recognizing it. It has very small, scale-like leaves arranged in tight rows along the twig, the individual leaves overlapping each other in shingle fashion along the twig; several such small twigs together form a flat spray several inches across and upward of nearly a foot in length. Most hikers know this species already under the name "arbor vitae," which nursery owners seem to prefer. The wild form is a small- to medium-size tree growing to about 30 feet high and occasionally to 2 feet in diameter. The crown of open-grown trees is very dense and pyramidal in form, with the branches retained nearly to the ground. Open-grown specimens have a clear, highly tapered, and often buttressed bole. The bark is stringy and fibrous in appearance, as in most species of the "cedar family." On live branches notice the small, erect cones with just four or six pairs of scales showing.

White-cedar is most commonly seen around watercourses in the high peak region. Wherever water occurs at or near the surface, at whatever elevation, white-cedar may be expected, even in crevices out on wet cliff faces.

Key: crown densely compact, bright green, symmetrically ovate, persisting close to ground when growing in open, becoming more oblong in age, often with two or more (hidden) trunks, the bark pale brown and stringy.

14. Eastern Redcedar *Juniperus virginiana*

Eastern Redcedar is the most widely distributed conifer in the eastern United States, but one would never guess it from its rarity in the high peak region. This is actually a lowland species, in our area confined to the two major river drainages on our eastern slopes, the Ausable and the Bouquet. South of Albany in the Hudson Valley there are thousands of young redcedars invading abandoned fields, as one can easily notice driving up the Thruway. Redcedar normally grows on sites too dry and infertile for other tree species; it thus may act as a pioneer, in time improving the site sufficiently for other trees to come in. Where you find pasture or old-field juniper—a sure sign of depleted, impoverished soil—you may also find our redcedar.

Eastern Redcedar is a small tree at best, rarely exceeding 25

Eastern Redcedar. Eastern Redcedar trees are even smaller than those of Northern White-cedar, and rarely exceed twenty feet or so in height. The foliage color varies from dark green to purplish depending upon the time of year.

feet in height. The trees typically are columnar in shape, though with age their form becomes conical as the lower branches grow outward. Redcedar differs from all other eastern conifers in having two types of foliage. On most trees, over 90 percent of the leaves are the adult type—that is, scale-like and flattened against the twig. Leaves are slightly keeled down the middle, and this gives the twig a four-sided shape, so they can be rolled between the fingers much like a spruce needle. The other leaf type, called juvenile foliage, occurs on fast-growing branch tips and consists of awl-shaped leaves standing erect away from the twig in pairs on either side. The reproductive structures are borne on separate trees, so the small, berry-like "cones" identify a female plant; the tiny pollen cones of male trees are quickly shed and rarely seen, a situation similar to most conifers.

The nearest redcedars I know of in our region are several dozen scattered along the north side of Route 73, a mile and a half west of Keene on the Cascade Lake grade. Interestingly, pasture juniper is growing around the base of many of the trees. This latter conifer, although only a shrub, is noteworthy in itself, for it is the only species of conifer that occurs on all three of the northern continents—North America, Europe, and Asia. This particular station for the two junipers is a worthwhile stop. Otherwise, redcedars are common along Hardy Road in Wilmington, where the Jack Pines also may be seen.

Key: conical or irregularly shaped crown, dark or bluish green; female trees with conspicuously white spherical cones resembling berries; bark stringy.

15. Quaking Aspen *Populus tremuloides*

The key to understanding the natural history of Quaking Aspen is simply realizing that this is North America's arboreal "opportunist." It is our pioneer par excellence, the one species that on a continental scale moves in to take over a forest site following any natural disaster, especially wildfire. From Mexico northward to the Arctic, from eastern Canada across to Alaska, Quaking Aspen is the first tree to come in on lands where the forest has been damaged, removed or destroyed. Even where the organic layers of the soil have been consumed in fire, aspen is able to get established. Thus, in New York State wherever the loggers cleared the forest or fires blackened the landscape, a crop of aspen soon appeared—the first step, in many areas, in the slow march of vegetational recovery.

The current generation of hikers can little appreciate the contribution of aspen to the restoration of the Forest Preserve lands originally acquired by the state after logging and fires had left them "worthless." It was the aspen more than any other species that pioneered these thousands of acres. Aspen seeds, produced in profusion each May, are near-microscopic in size, the smallest and lightest of any hardwood, but they are each topped with a plume of fuzz, and so are carried great distances by the wind. Once a single tree is established it can further spread over the site by means of root suckers, new stems sent up by the roots a short distance away from the parent tree. Some of the clumps of aspen we see

Quaking Aspen. Before Quaking Aspen trees reach about a foot in diameter, the youthful smooth and pale olive-green bark develops scattered diamond-shaped cracks, which later spread both upwards and downwards along the trunk, thereby forming vertical crevices separating flat-topped ridges.

are genetically only one individual, a thicket derived some time in the past from a single seed.

The healing cover of Quaking Aspen initiates the succession of trees toward a climax forest, but the aspen itself will not be there when the process is completed. Aspen is among our most intolerant species; it has to have full sunlight to prosper. As the trees grow taller and shade the ground, they render the site unfavorable for their own seedlings. Now mid-tolerant species colonize the site, and in time the long-lasting climax species will return. Meanwhile, the sun-loving aspen has moved on to other disturbed areas where upsets in the natural balance have created new openings.

You may recognize Quaking Aspen with your ears because the rustle of aspen leaves is one of the most distinctive sounds in second-growth woods. (By how much do the natural sounds of the forest make hiking more rewarding?) The leaf stalks of the aspen are flattened rather than round, so the leaf blades tremble in the slightest breeze. Aspen leaves are relatively small, averaging about 2 inches in length, and are egg-shaped in outline. The margin has very small, rounded teeth. The leaves are a lovely light green in the early spring, the softest color to be seen on any Adirondack hardwood; as the summer progresses, the color shifts toward a gray-green; and in the fall they turn a beautiful golden-yellow, quite as striking as the hue of their neighbors the birch. Curiously, Quaking Aspen is the first tree species to leaf out in the spring and the last one to turn color in the fall.

The bark of aspen, too, is very distinctive: greenish white to pale olive, occasionally even silvery, on vigorous young growth. It stays smooth until the trunk is nearly a foot thick. The crown is quite open and accordingly casts less shade than perhaps any other hardwood. Being intolerant and requiring full sunlight to function properly, leaves on the lower shaded branches soon die and then the branches fall, so that aspen trees generally have clear boles when growing in the woods. Unfortunately, the trees are short-lived, rarely exceeding 50 feet in height.

For all its post-fire aggressiveness, aspen still is confined to the lower elevations, rarely going upslope above 2500 feet, but lots of it is seen around Heart Lake or Marcy Dam. You may hear some people refer to Quaking Aspen as a worthless "weed" tree, but every citizen of New York State can be thankful that we had it to speed up the return of forest cover following the logging of yesteryear.

Key: young bark smooth, pale olive-green, often with a whitish bloom, in age darkening and developing flat-topped ridges.

16. Bigtooth Aspen *Populus grandidentata*

In discussing Northern White-cedar we noted that it was morphologically identical throughout its range but ecologically divided into two races. With the aspen we have a reverse case: two species morphologically distinct but ecologically identical. Bigtooth Aspen in no ecologically significant way differs from Quaking Aspen. What one does, the other does; where one occurs, the other is found, though Bigtooth generally in much lower numbers. The only discernible differences are that Bigtooth is slightly longer-lived and consequently somewhat larger, holds on longer before

Bigtooth Aspen. Young trunks of Bigtooth Aspen differ from those of Quaking Aspen solely in their darker olive-green coloration; in maturity, the two look alike. Bigtooth trees however may reach 30" in DBH (diameter at breast height) whereas Quaking rarely exceeds 20".

dying out, and is not quite as abundant as its smaller brother—but there the differences end.

Bigtooth Aspen leaves are twice as large as Quaking, and they are bordered with large, rounded teeth. When they first emerge from the bud, which usually is about ten days later than in Quaking Aspen, the leaves are covered with a whitish fuzz, but this disappears by early June. Quaking Aspen leaves, by contrast, are a shiny green, the new ones sometimes tinged with a faint copper color. The bark of Bigtooth is somewhat darker, but not obviously so. If you study the aspens in late May just about the time Quaking Aspen leaves are fully expanded, the fruit may be seen as it is about to shed its seeds. Each fruit is a small capsule the size of a tiny pea; about two or three dozen are strung together on a stalk 4–6 inches long. As the greenish capsules dry out and open, the fuzzy seeds drift through the air like miniature dandelion seeds.

Most of the post-fire aspens (both species) in the high peak region have reached maturity and are slowly dying out. On the other hand, aspens are always around, getting started in new sunny spots. Except in mature, closed-canopy forests, you'll have no trouble finding these two pioneers.

Key: similar to Quaking Aspen but the young bark darker and more yellowish brown.

17. Balsam Poplar *Populus balsamifera*

You know when you are near aspens by the rustle of their leaves. But this particular species of Populus is one you can tell by the aroma in the air. The buds, and then the leaves as they unfold, are coated with a fragrant orange-brown resin which the sensitive nose can detect a quarter mile downwind. This species and our native fir possess the most distinctive aromas in the north woods, and each gets its name "balsam" from that fact.

Balsam Poplar is another fast-growing, intolerant pioneer species, nearly as widely distributed in northern North America as Quaking Aspen but not nearly as abundant with us. In the boreal forests of Canada it is the tallest, largest hardwood tree, commonly attaining a height of 80 feet and diameter of nearly 3 feet. This is a moisture-loving tree most common on wet sites, but in our climate of abundant moisture the trees occur on a variety of sites and, for that matter, of elevations. It reacts to disturbance much as aspen does and, similarly, forms local pure stands by means of root suckers, especially on sandy soils.

Balsam Poplar may be recognized by its leaves, which are identical in shape with lilac: round at the bottom, tapered to an acute point at the tip. The margin is only obscurely toothed. The most unusual feature of the leaf, however, is the color, which turns to a golden-brown hue as the season progresses, so it is easy to spot this tree when driving through the Adirondacks in the second half of the season. Yet the underside of the leaf is very light-colored; in fact, the lower surface is so whitish that the darker veins can be seen branching throughout the leaf tissue. Moreover, the underside is usually blotchy with some of the orangish-brown resin—a third color feature by which the foliage may be recognized. The bark is of darker brown than in the aspens; on both young and old trees the valleys between the vertically aligned ridges are

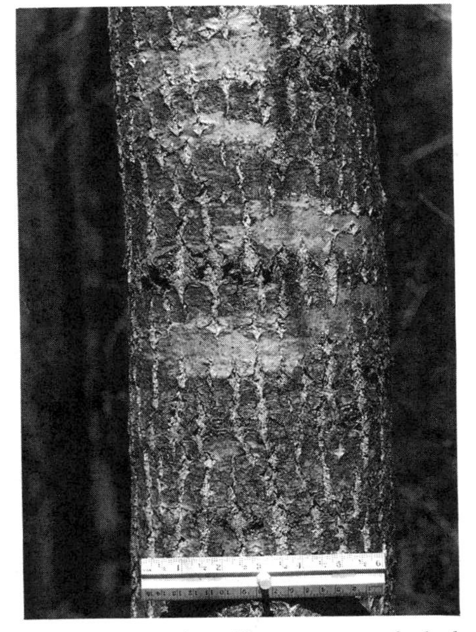

Balsam Poplar. The whitish underbark of Balsam Poplar becomes quite evident as soon as the bark begins to fissure in early age, in the same sequence as in the Aspens, and may remain visible on the sides of the cracks into old age.

conspicuously whitened. The buds are quite large, about two-thirds of an inch long, and very sticky owing to the abundant resin. Once smelled, the resin is never forgotten—it is that unusual. Touch the bud lightly and you can smell it on your hand all day.

Balsam Poplar is widely distributed in the high peak region, but limited to successional stands and thus quite sporadic in occurrence. Look for it wherever the fires of 1903 swept the intermountain landscape, such as around the Cascade Lakes and Keene Valley. It does not venture very high on the slopes, rarely above 2000 ft. elevation.

Key: young bark olive-green, aromatic when cut, developing diamond shaped, white-sided cracks; older bark becoming ridged with faint white lines between ridges.

18. Eastern Hophornbeam *Ostrya virginiana*

Hophornbeam is not what we think of as an Adirondack mountain species. True, it is a common understory species throughout most of the deciduous forests to the south, but here it is far out of its climate and is relatively infrequent. When it does occur it grows mostly on richer soils either of the Hardwood Site-Type or where fertile organic materials have accumulated over the glacial drift. It is nowhere abundant, and rarely if ever, to my knowledge, does it occur above 2000 ft. elevation.

Hophornbeam is actually easy to recognize. It is a small tree, to 40 feet in height and a foot in diameter, and our only tree with a shreddy bark—bark with narrow, vertical strips broken every few

Eastern Hophornbeam. The conspicuous out-turned strips and scales of Eastern Hophornbeam start to develop once the trunks reach four inches in diameter, and thereafter remain evident into old age even though the exposed tips eventually weather off, leaving just the vertical ridges.

inches into scales that turn out at both top and bottom. The leaves resemble those of a Yellow Birch but are thinner in texture, widest in the middle, and slightly hairy on the upper surface. The fruit cannot be mistaken: it resembles clusters of hops, as are used in brewing beer.

For all practical purposes one can forget about hophornbeam when on the mountainsides. The nearest specimen to Heart Lake that I know of is a single tree with five stems from the base, about an eighth of a mile beyond the height of land toward South Meadows from the Heart Lake Road. Numerous trees are seen along the lower section of Spruce Hill Road east of Keene. It is frequent also along the lower section of Johns Brook.

On the other hand, the species may be locally abundant on fertile sites "off the anorthosite," that is, where the bedrock is one of the metasedimentary type that produce richer soils, such as those selected by the earlier settlers as suitable for farming in the Vermontville area. West of Catamount Mountain, where limestone rocks appear at the surface, such lime-preferring species as basswood, American Elm, and hophornbeam are quite frequent. I have also encountered hophornbeam in old-growth stands near Saranac Lake and at Cranberry Lake, but always as single, isolated trees.

A closely related species, American Hornbeam, *Carpinus caroliniana*, may be found at one isolated spot in our region, along the east branch of the Ausable River between Jay and Keene Valley. It, too, is a small tree, and it also has leaves resembling a Yellow Birch, except they are narrower. The big distinction between these two relatives is the bark, as the still-rarer American Hornbeam has smooth gray bark with ridges and flutings resembling taut muscles, whence one other common name, Musclewood. Some folks know the latter species as Blue Beech (though "gray beech" would more accurately describe the color of the bark) or Water Beech because of its confinement to streamsides and lake shores. Both species were prized by farmers for their strong wood, as suitable for tool handles as was hickory.

Key: young bark soon developing narrow vertical strips, turning up at ends persisting with age.

19. Paper Birch *Betula papyrifera*

Every hiker in the High Peak region knows the story behind our beautiful stands of Paper Birch: wildfire. Practically every stand of Paper Birch is living testimony to the occurrence of fire in that general area sometime in the past—usually severe fire that burned everything down to the bare mineral soil or destroyed the ground cover so severely that subsequent erosion removed the fertile organic layer. This same situation brings in aspen, but in the high peak region the Paper Birch is far more prevalent for two reasons. First, although the species parallel each other in all other ecological respects, Paper Birch is better adapted to the cooler climates and shorter growing season of the mountain slopes and higher elevations: it alone among hardwoods remains tree-like to the timberline. Second, the birch sheds its seeds slowly over a period of two or three months, from the fall into winter. This means that the shifting autumn winds and winter storms will blow the light seed in all directions away from a tree, and because the parent birch was scattered from place to place on the slope to start with, the landscape is within a year or two saturated with its seed.

Paper Birch seed germinates quickly in the spring—even on top of the melting snow—and thus quickly becomes established. Over a period of three or four years a dense stand of young Paper Birch may cover a site, protecting the ground from further damage. The proof of this aggressiveness is everywhere evident in the high peak region. Entire once-burned slopes are now covered by pure Paper Birch stands.

When hiking through one of these birch forests, notice what is coming in on the forest floor: Red Spruce and Balsam Fir. Birch, being intolerant of shade, does not follow itself on a site. Rather, the spruce and fir (climax species here) return immediately, without an intervening stage of mid-tolerant sub-climax species. The quick return reflects the absence at such elevations of other competing hardwoods.

One further point should be made about the Paper Birch. Although it is ecologically uniform across its range (all Canadian forests plus our northern fringe of states), its leaves are extremely variable from region to region. The leaf shape seen at lower elevations—nearly round but tapered at the tip—is the one most typical of the species, but as we go up the slopes to higher elevations it acquires a heart-shaped base and a longer point at the tip. This latter form is recognized by botanists as Mountain Paper Birch (*Betula papyrifera*, variety *cordifolia*) and is the characteristic birch at about 2500 feet. In recent years some authors have been treating it as a separate species, *Betula cordifolia*. Notice that the exfoliation of its whitish outer bark reveals an inner layer much

Paper Birch (left leaf), Mountain Paper Birch (right leaf). Twigs and stems of paper Birch are at first reddish brown but at 1–2" diameter the outer layers curl off to reveal the characteristic white bark typical of older growth.

more reddish in color than in the lowland variety. Otherwise, the two are similar in general appearance.

Paper Birch is one of the most abundant hardwoods in the high peak region. You might wish to examine the change in leaf shape at progressively higher elevations as you approach timberline.

Key: young stems reddish brown, at 2-inch thickness peeling and turning white except for blackish scars at top and sides of trunk where main branches leave trunk; peeling or curling in wide strips with time and revealing orangish underbark; portions often darkening at maturity.

20. Yellow Birch *Betula alleghaniensis*

Yellow Birch is one of the more valuable northern hardwoods in Adirondack forests. Individual high-quality logs are equal in value to prime sugar maple logs. In the primeval forests of the region, Yellow Birch was the tallest hardwood, some trees growing to 100 feet tall and more than 4 feet in diameter. Today one has to scour one of the few remaining parcels of virgin growth to find a tree that size. The largest I have seen is a 56-inch-diameter specimen near Saranac Lake.

To ecologists, Yellow Birch is the most typical Adirondack hardwood, much as Red Spruce is the most representative of the conifers. The reason for this high esteem is not its premier economic position but the fact that Yellow Birch here is at the same time both a mid-tolerant species capable of withstanding moderate competition and the most aggressive species on the most number of

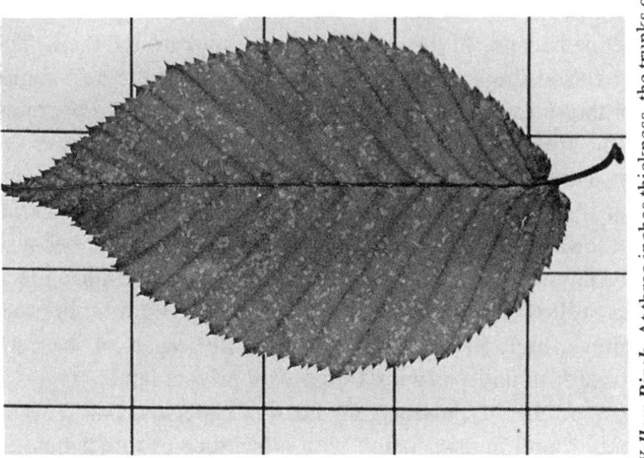

Yellow Birch. At three inches thickness, the trunks of Yellow Birch bark turn a bronze or yellowish color as the surface layers start to peal backwards in tight curls. However, once the trunk reaches about a foot in diameter the curls weather off completely and reveal a thick, platy outer bark, irregularly cracked.

diverse sites. In brief, excepting the spruce-fir belt, Yellow Birch can grow in practically any forest situation, much like a pioneer species, and yet does not give up its position there without an ecological fight. In time, of course, our two most tolerant hardwoods, American Beech and Sugar Maple, will replace it, but Yellow Birch is so aggressive it keeps coming back whenever the slightest disturbance creates an opening. In the natural forests there are just enough disturbances for Yellow Birch to maintain its numbers and positions in essentially all forest types, even on hummocks around swamps.

But every biological success has its built-in control, and in Yellow Birch this is its "sensitivity," once it is established, to further site change. Trees are easily damaged by anything that upsets the immediate environment around the tree. For example, following the blowdown of November 1950, thousands of Yellow Birch went into decline because of the opening of the stand around them. The opening raised the soil temperature, or dried out the soil somewhat, or the sun scalded the trunks, or the greater wind movement rocked the trees too much, or something happened to cause the trees to lose vigor. Thus it is axiomatic among commercial loggers that if there is any Yellow Birch of marginally commercial size on the site being cut, this might as well be taken too, because it will die anyway. Yet, according to many professional Adirondack foresters, Yellow Birch is one of the species of the future. In time, they believe, high-quality Yellow Birch will be part of the economic base for quality sawlog forestry on private lands.

Yellow birch is typically a mixed-stand species; that is, it is commonly found in association with other species rather than in pure stands. It is almost universally present in second-growth Adirondack forests. The trees are recognized by the golden-gray to bronze-colored bark with its papery strips curling back horizontally around the stem. The leaves are much more elliptical than in Paper Birch and resemble those of elm. To check the identification, scratch the twig and smell it: the fragrance of oil of wintergreen confirms your identification.

Key: young bark developing slender yellow-gray curls, later becoming smooth, then in age breaking into scales and plates, highly variable.

21. Gray Birch *Betula populifolia*

Gray Birch competes in a figurative sense with Fire Cherry and mountain-ash for the title of Smallest Tree in the Adirondacks. Trees are rarely over 20 feet tall—the minimum height, by common agreement, for calling a woody plant a tree. Moreover, several stems often come up as a clump from one root system; when this happens, the stem arches sidewise and then swings upward in the battle for dominance, each often crooked and no one ever seeming to gain any great advantage. At other times, single stems develop as on most other species, but even here there is generally a lean to the trees. Because of this tendency to tilt to one side, Gray Birch is very susceptible to snow damage; many young stands quickly deteriorate as snow, weighing down the leaning stems, snaps them off. Such a damaged stand may look like a jungle.

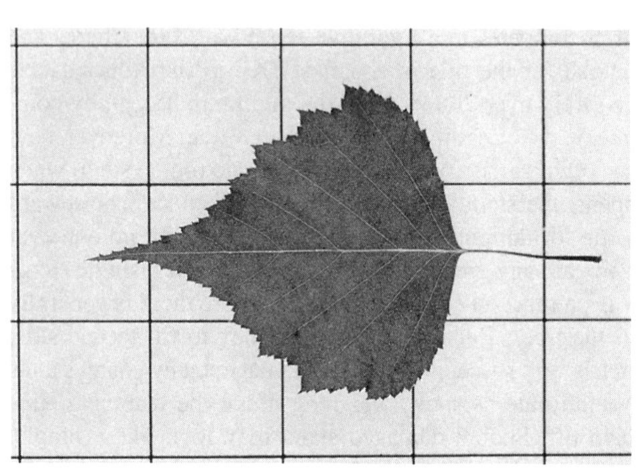

Gray Birch. Gray Birch bark is a chalky white color and trees do not develop large limbs as do other hardwood species, rather small branches arise directly from the main trunk. The trunk bark directly below the origin of the branches becomes roughened and turns into a conspicuous black patch.

In our area Gray Birch seems to come in more often as sporadic individual pioneers than as waves of trees such as are seen elsewhere in New York and New England.

The ecology of Gray Birch is the same as for Paper Birch, but this shorter-lived species is even more characteristic of impoverished sites. There probably is no hardwood in the Adirondacks better able to withstand dry, sterile soils than Gray Birch. The only reason we don't see more of it is its extreme intolerance—it must have full sunlight to grow. Where it is found in great numbers the soils are probably deep sands.

When first seen Gray Birch may be confused with Paper Birch, for it has similar white bark. But Gray Birch is more of a chalky white, does not peel, and has black triangular scars where the branches leave the main stem. The small leaves are triangular in shape, unlike those of any other species in the region.

Gray Birch is infrequent in our immediate area, though it is widely distributed, and in places common, in the Adirondack flat country. Look for it on sandy road banks, ditches, or fields of former farmlands. It sometimes appears unexpectedly along small streams.

Key: young bark resembling Paper Birch but remaining chalky white and with more blackish scars where branches leave trunk; lacking large limbs.

22. American Beech *Fagus grandifolia*

In Adirondack forests, American Beech is one of the two most tolerant hardwoods, and accordingly is a climax species. Ecologists refer, in fact, to the non-mountainous sections of the Northeast as being a Beech-Birch-Maple-Hemlock region, recognizing these four species as the long-lasting dominants throughout. Beech occurs on almost any site in the intervening areas between the lowland swamps and the high elevation spruce-fir belt; it will be found with other hardwoods or in mixtures with several of the conifers. Its only major environmental requirement is for fairly moist but well-drained soils, for it is a shallow-rooted species. On the other hand, it will not grow where the soils are saturated, as around bogs and swamps.

Beech is much under discussion these days among forest-land owners. It has become "controversial" because it is susceptible to serious heart rot and butt rot, which may not be evident outside the tree. Loggers therefore don't like it; and sawmill operators dislike it because it is difficult to season properly. For a number of years this species has been left standing in the woods while others have been removed, but now it is a desirable species for hardwood pulp.

Beech spreads vigorously by means of root suckers, just like an aspen, and quickly fills in any openings that may develop on the site. Deer will not eat the leaves, although they browse nearly every other broad-leaf tree or shrub in the woods. Meanwhile, a bark disease has impacted the larger beech trees over the past four decades and continues to spread slowly, further complicating management of the species.

Beech wood is only so-so in value for manufactured products or pulping; in recent years it has become valuable for fuel wood, which, however, represents low economic value. In terms of aesthetics, beech is an impressive tree. The average mature tree is about 80 feet tall, about 2 feet in diameter, and has live branches persisting

American Beech. Beech bark (viewed up close) has small, inconspicuous bumps on its surface, each with a faint line passing vertically over the top of the bump. Further, being a shade tolerant species, trees in new stands may have occasional side twigs persisting along the lower trunk.

nearly to the base. The trunk is as easy to spot from a short distance as birch because of the smooth, slate-gray bark. Up close the elliptical leaves, about 5 inches long, reveal a small tooth at the end of each side vein, but the rest of the margin is smooth. The buds catch the eye because they are many times longer than broad and thus resemble little spears. In the fall the characteristic beech fruit, two triangular-shaped nuts borne in a small husk with weak spines, may be seen on the ground. This is the time of year, too, when beech can be recognized by the copper-colored leaves the same general color one sees in the oak country farther south of New York.

For all the debate on its economic merits, American Beech is one of the most characteristic and most beautiful trees in the high peak region. The annual crop of nuts helps to carry many species of wildlife through the winter months. Grown in the open, beech makes a superior ornamental for the home owner. Trees are easily grown from seed.

Key: bark remaining gray and smooth throughout life.

23. Northern Red Oak *Quercus rubra*

Yes, we do have an oak in our region! The oaks are typically southern (and western) hardwoods, characteristic of the warm temperate-zone climates but not of the cold, boreal climates of northern New York and Canada. As an exception to the rule, Northern Red Oak penetrates the Adirondacks along several river courses, including the Ausable along Route 9. (Actually, it bypasses most of the uplands here and continues into Ontario and Quebec.) In the

Northern Red Oak. The bark of young Northern Red Oak appears smooth and taut; then in age, vertical crevices develop and thereby produce flat-topped ridges; and lastly when mature, large ridges extend up and down the full trunk length.

eastern Adirondack region it is confined mostly to the lower slopes facing Lake Champlain, such as on Whiteface Mountain, where it reaches 2000 feet elevation. It occurs between Black Brook and Silver Lake, on Catamount Mountain, and on a few low hills near Keene, but it does not penetrate far into the interior. The occurrence of Red Oak at several locations in the central Adirondacks, such as at Goodnow Mountain near Newcomb, is attributed to relict stands that have survived on warm slopes since the glacial maximum period several thousand years ago.

If you can recognize a tree as an oak, that will be enough for present purposes, since we have only the one species in the high peak region. But be warned that several others occur around the periphery of the Adirondack Park. All oaks have oblong leaves lobed on the margin. In the White Oak group the lobes are round; in the Red Oak group, toothed. Northern Red Oak leaves, specifically, are rectangular in outline and have about nine pointed lobes. When the leaves first emerge from the bud in the spring, they are often tinged with scarlet; in the fall they are russet. The acorns are among the largest of oaks but are borne on a shallow cup, and are noted for their high percent of germination. The bark of the trees is variable but typically features smooth but irregular ridges that intertwine at short distances along the trunk.

Key: bark dull to dark gray, in age developing flat, distantly interlacing ridges.

24. American Elm *Ulmus americana*

American Elm is another one of those lowland visitors in the high peak region. The hiker is not likely to see it in the woods or on the slopes, but rather in second growth forests of the flatlands between the mountains. In other sections of the state, elm is a subclimax species on wet ground such as near watercourses or in meadows. Just enough trees are found in Adirondack forests to indicate it

American Elm. The gray bark of young American Elm quickly develops irregular cracks and fissures. Subsequent weathering of the bark surface reveals the characteristic underbark with several corky white layers within. Before maturity, distantly interlacing ridges appear and persist into old age.

was here as a sporadic tree prior to the heyday of the logger, not just a recent invader from ornamental trees of town and city. In the Cranberry Lake area trees occur deep in the forest 12 miles from the nearest road of any sort, and at 2100-ft. elevation, but these are exceptions.

Everyone can recognize mature American Elm; its vase-shape has a more distinctive silhouette, by far, than any other eastern hardwood. Younger trees are easily recognized by the speckled appearance of the bark owing to the whitish inner layers becoming exposed through weathering of the otherwise gray-black surface layer. The leaves are elliptical but conspicuously unequal or lopsided at the base; the margin is sharply toothed, with teeth of varying size; the upper surface bears stiff hairs; and the texture is almost leathery. To check the identification, cut into the bark and see the alternating layers of buff and reddish brown.

American Elm requires moist and rich soils for good growth and is surprisingly frequent as a subclimax species along roadsides and power lines and other untended places returning to forested conditions. On the other hand, it rarely appears on sloping landscape, and thus is unexpected when climbing the peaks. Our Adirondack trees seem to be escaping the dutch elm disease that afflicts them in urban areas, where they once grew in dense populations as streeet ornamentals.

Key: bark quickly becoming rough and irregularly ridged, in age with alternating layers of buff and darker tissue when cut or exposed.

25. American Mountain-ash *Sorbus americana*

For many mountain hikers American Mountain-ash is the frosting on the arboreal cake. The constant forest of spruce and fir and Paper Birch, all too common on our higher burned mountainsides, does become a bit monotonous at times. Only the occasional mountain-ash breaks the repetition from stand to stand. Where Paper Birch got established, so too did the mountain-ash, but in much fewer numbers. Its fleshy seed is heavy, and it can travel great distances only via the stomach of a Canada jay or a few other birds. Moreover, it fruits less heavily and less frequently. Otherwise, the two like the same disturbed sites, areas free of other competitors. The mountain-ash is less hardy than birch and gets smaller quicker toward the summit. In fact, at timberline mountain-ash acts like a spreading bush.

Mountain-ash makes up for its small stature by being one of our loveliest trees, in fact an excellent ornamental. Each June it has the most beautiful panoply of flowers of any Adirondack hardwood, bright clusters of snow-white flowers 6–8 inches across. In autumn these turn into deep-red "berries," resembling cranberries, that persist into the winter months. A stalk of mountain-ash "berries" lightly coated with fresh snow in October seems to mark the end of each growing season on the higher slopes. But the trees are lovely at all times of the year: smoothish gray bark with gigantic orangish lenticels; long purple buds, as unusual as those of any hardwood; and particularly the feathery, compound leaves. These leaves have 13–17 small oblong, toothed leaflets, similar more to sumac than to the ash. Of course, this is not really an ash; true

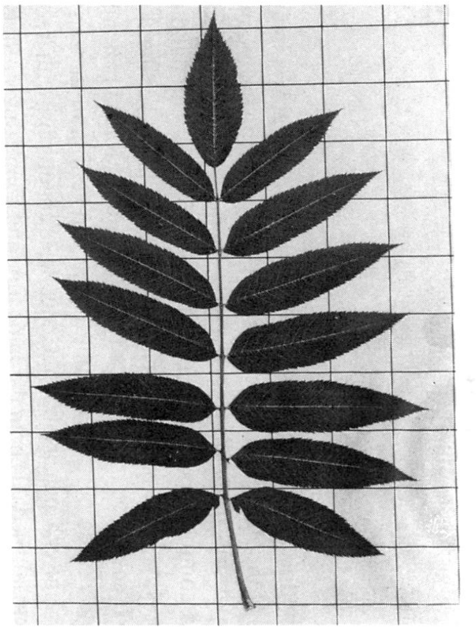

American Mountain-ash. The bark of young American Mountain-ash is quite smooth, but wide lenticels appear as horizontal breaks in the bark, and in age become lens-shaped and may show their orangish interiors if lightly scratched. In fully mature trees, the entire bark becomes scaly and orange-brown.

ashes belong to a completely different family and have their leaves (only 7–9 leaflets) arranged in opposite pairs rather than set individually along the twig as in mountain-ash.

This species also occurs as an infrequent tree of wet sites, stream banks, and lakesides across the entire Adirondacks. Cold climate and infertile soils do not trouble it. But the tree is intolerant and won't grow long in the shade. Mountain-ash seedlings are nearly everywhere—that is, where the birds happened to drop them—but they must have full sunlight to grow to any size. Mountain-ash is found on almost any burn in the high country. The north side of Rocky Peak Ridge is covered with it, and in the late fall, with the leaves turned a beautiful orange-yellow, the whole side of the mountain appears at sunset to be afire with red.

Key: bark gray, relatively smooth, turning black and developing prominent orangish, elliptical lenticels.

26. Black Cherry *Prunus serotina*

A distribution map of Black Cherry will show that it grows in all sections of the state, but in fact it is rather uncommon in the mountainous portions of the high peak region. To the west and south of us it is a common species of second-growth forests. Throughout northern New York, when the original cover was logged or the site burned, Black Cherry was typically one of three or four subclimax species to invade quickly without the site's reverting to the early pioneer stage of aspen and birch. Under these conditions, with trees getting established all about the same time and competing strongly,

Black Cherry. Black Cherry is an eye-catcher both for the blackness of its bark and for the tightly packed large scales with out-turned edges. Break off one of the scales, though, and you'll see the bright orange-brown underbark. The scales persist unchanged into and through old age.

the cherry grows tall and straight. And, the tree being relatively intolerant, its lower branches are soon shed, leaving a clear bole. These are the valuable sawlog trees from which quality furniture is made. Hardwood pulping mills generally will not accept more than a little cherry in the truckloads they buy; the dark wood is too difficult to bleach.

Black Cherry is notorious for being the one Adirondack hardwood most influenced by the environment under which it is growing. True, with nurse trees crowded around it, it will grow as treelike as the best, but put it in the open and it becomes as bushy as a lilac. These bushy trees may be valuable as a temporary cover but not for much else.

Probably more Black Cherry and White Ash grow in the Adirondacks now than a hundred years ago. Although hardy in our cold climates, Black Cherry is more at home with oaks and hickories in the warmer climates farther south; it is frequent throughout the eastern temperate zone and even continues southward into Mexico. When we do see it in our mountainous country, it can't be missed: it has black scaly bark, the darkest and roughest of our hardwoods. The bark on young trees is already black but remains smooth. Notice the lenticels on these younger stems; they look like horizontal white pencil markings, over an inch long in cases. The narrow, elliptical leaves are undistinguished except for a band of orange fuzz along the mid-rib on the lower surface of the leaf. The blackish fruit, maturing in late summer, is actually quite edible and makes a delicious jam or wine—take your pick.

Good specimens may be seen when walking through late successional forests in the low country of the high peak region, particularly where the fires of 1903 produced dense pioneering stands that forced the Black Cherries to grow tall and straight.

Key: bark at first smooth, with small white lenticels, then breaking into small blackish, out-turned scales, orangish on under surface.

27. Fire Cherry *Prunus pennsylvanica*

Fire Cherry is known also as Bird Cherry and Pin Cherry. The first two of these names are particularly appropriate because this species is a frequent pioneer after fire and is brought in by birds eating the fruit. Like most pioneers, it is a short-lived species that grows very fast for maybe 20 years, then slows down and soon drops out of the picture. This is regrettable, for under good growth conditions it is one of our most attractive trees and would otherwise make an excellent ornamental.

The Fire Cherry is seen only where there has been some severe disturbance in recent years. It is quickly shaded out along our trails when the canopy closes in above. Accordingly, most of the trees seen in New York State are in hedgerows or open ground where competition is at a minimum. As an average, it takes only about 25 years for the trees to be over-topped when they are pioneering forest situations.

Fire Cherry is actually our only cherry that really looks like one with respect to color. The twigs are cherry-red, and so is the young trunk if the trees are growing alone in the sun—a lustrous rusty cherry color just like that of the polished wood. On the living bark notice the warty lenticels, perhaps a quarter of an inch

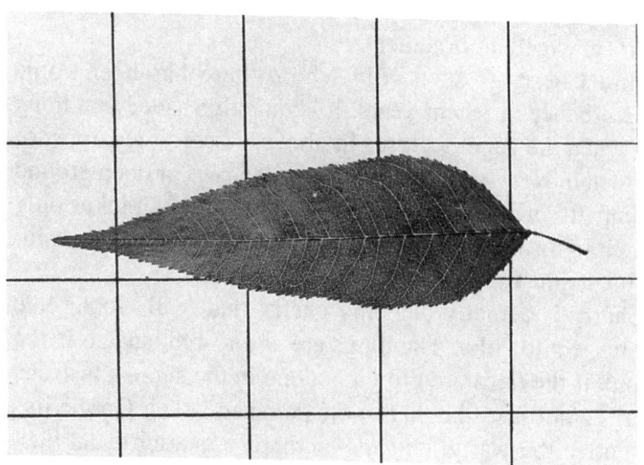

Fire Cherry. Fire Cherry growing in the woods is blackish and shiny with lenticels that are knobby and extremely wide horizontally, of the same blackish color as the surrounding bark, some reaching over 4" across. The bark surface otherwise remains as tight and smooth as that of youth.

long; scratch one with a fingernail and you expose the bright orange tissue inside.

On the other hand, Fire Cherry in dense or shaded growing conditions seems to produce a surprisingly blackish bark. There is nothing especially distinctive about the leaves, however; they are the size and shape of a narrow Indian arrowhead with a rounded base. The fruit is bright red, more attractive than Black Cherry but actually very bitter. The twigs of all species of cherry smell similarly bitter or pungent.

Along the trails in the Paper Birch forest Fire Cherry appears occasionally, even at fairly high elevations. It came in at 3800 feet on the Algonquin trail following the blowdown of 1950. At one time it was present where we now find second-growth stands of Yellow Birch, aspen, and Red Maple at lower elevations throughout the high peak region, but it has since been shaded out. If in the woods you happen to see, under a closed canopy, standing trunks of dead trees perhaps 6–8 inches in diameter, the tops commonly gone and with absolutely black bark but with large, eye-shaped lenticels, these are old Fire Cherries shaded out by longer-living associates. Fire Cherry may still be found in the same type of open, brushy areas as the more common Black Cherry.

Key: bark variable, from lustrous cinnamon brown when fast-growing in sun to blackish when suppressed; in age developing large, conspicuous, eye-shaped lenticels.

28. Shadbush *Amelanchier arborea*

Several species of shadbush (serviceberry, juneberry) grow in New York State, mostly as shrubs. One species, however, easily reaches tree size when mature. It happens to occur in two forms or varieties, once considered separate species: Downy Shadbush, with leaves covered briefly with a whitish fuzz the first two weeks in spring as they expand, and smooth Shadbush, with leaves entirely devoid of hairs. Shadbush trees are about 25 feet tall at maturity in our area and would be hardly noticeable but for the fact that they are the first trees to flower conspicuously in the spring. (We say "conspicuously" because the petals quickly fall and litter the trails we follow.) The flowers are about an inch across, of five strap-like, snow-white petals, appearing before the leaves are out. Several hundred such flowers may appear on a single tree. Shadbush signals the opening of buds of all other trees in the region. Three other species of serviceberry, all infrequent shrubs, also occur in our region, with one, Bartrams Serviceberry, reaching timberline.

One who is not in the woods in May to see the Shadbush in flower may have a hard time locating trees to examine, because the leaves are not especially eye-catching. They are of an ordinary egg shape or oblong in outline, finely toothed, about 2 to 3 inches long and half that in width. One should look for the bark when seeking one's first tree. It looks just like young beech, smooth and slate-gray, except here there are indistinct blackish or lavender lines running vertically on the trunk. Curiously, the buds also look like beech, though much smaller and with fewer scales.

Shadbush is an intolerant species occurring at the edge of woods,

Shadbush. Shadbush when growing as solitary stems looks like a small Maple or Beech sapling but the smooth gray bark soon develops distinctive vertical and lavender lines. In old age the bark near the trunk base becomes as extremely rough and blackish as that of mid-age White Ash.

at roadsides, or in other semi-open situations. Like Fire Cherry, it will quickly die out when shaded. The largest trees I have seen are about 6 inches in diameter and barely 30 feet tall. Practically all the Shadbushes that once occurred on the Algonquin trail are now dead and gone, but many still persist along the trail up Mt. Jo.

Key: bark remaining smooth and gray, developing inconspicuous purplish vertical lines.

29. Sugar Maple *Acer saccharum*

Have no doubts about it: Sugar Maple is the queen of Adirondack hardwoods. Granted, Yellow Birch is nearly as valuable at the moment on a log-for-log basis, is more aggressive after stand disturbance, and occurs on an even greater variety of sites; but on those areas most suited for hardwoods, the Hardwood Site–Type, Sugar Maple is the more abundant and dominant species. It is the most tolerant hardwood in the forest, surpassed by none and equaled only perhaps by beech. For this reason alone, Sugar Maple is the most abundant tree in New York State. It will survive under any canopy condition. On better sites it will grow as fast as most other hardwoods. On poorer sites, where conifers may be more aggressive, it often is overtopped, yet still holds on, growing slowly. Being a long-lived species, it eventually gets up to the sun.

Sugar Maple is one of our most vigorous reproducers, except for only a few of the short-lived pioneers. After a good seed year the forest floor may be literally a carpet of seedlings—you can't take a step without trampling some. Everywhere on the forest floor, Sugar Maple seems to be taking over the forest—and in fact *it is*, to a degree. The seedlings are so tolerant they will stand there for years, putting on only a few inches a year, before giving up. If the canopy does become open by the death of a nearby dominant or for some other reason, the seedlings then getting some sunlight will start growing faster and eventually reach the crown level. If no opening appears during the life of the seedling, by then another, younger crop has got started. Sooner or later, Sugar Maple is bound to come through, regardless of what species was initially growing on the site. "Patience" is its watchword.

Sugar Maple. Sugar Maple in the 6" to 12" range of diameter often proves to be a difficult tree to recognize on bark alone because of its great variability, ranging from trees that are just starting to develop rough bark (left) to others that are separated into shallow ridges covered with multiple scales (right).

To a degree this tree responds to light much as Black Cherry does. In the forest it may grow to 80 or 90 feet, with perhaps 30 feet of clear stem; in the open the trees quickly branch out in all directions from a short trunk. The amount of sap that can be tapped from a tree is in direct ratio to the amount of live crown.

The closer a forest is to the mature, climax state, the more Sugar Maple there is in it. If you start down the trail from Heart Lake toward Marcy Dam, for example, the first half mile of trail is over badly burned land in an early stage of forest recovery: large aspen now decadent in old age; poorly formed Red Maple of sprout origin; and the usual brushy growth of such post-fire conditions. But down opposite the Whale's Tail, halfway to the dam, the trail goes through an unburned section. Note the tall, dominant trees in it—mostly Sugar Maple.

Maples are recognized by the characteristic lobed leaves, the lobes being arranged like fingers on a palm. The leaves occur in pairs, one on either side of the twig. In Sugar Maple the several lobes, either three or five, may have two or three lesser points between them, but the margin is otherwise smooth. Sugar Maple comes into flower in early spring when the leaves are just unfolding; in fact, part of that pale yellow-green aura of a budding maple in May is due to the yellow flowers. The winged seeds do not mature until August or September, at which time they may be very evident all over the ground. In the fall this tree turns the familiar orange-red—more subtle than the Red Maple's.

If you don't know Sugar Maple, get acquainted. It is the State Tree of New York. Plenty of magnificent specimens may be found on the south side of Heart Lake in an area that escaped the fire. For that matter, you can't escape seeing Sugar Maple for long anywhere on the lower mountain sides where the soils remain fertile and moist.

Key: bark grayish, becoming irregularly ridged in age.

30. Red Maple *Acer rubrum*

According to the U.S. Forest Service, Red Maple is the most abundant and widely distributed hardwood in the forests of the United States. If any hardwood occurs on a site, a few trees of Red Maple are likely to be there. Sites include even the bogs and swamps where hardwoods generally are replaced by conifers. Of all our broad-leaved trees, Red Maple is best able to grow where its roots are constantly submerged. It frequently pioneers the floating mat which encircles bogs in the hill and lake country of the western Adirondacks, there seeming well at home with Tamarack and Black Spruce.

The surprising thing is that it can still grow on dry sites, such as where White Pine dominates the stand. Red Maple has the same broad latitude for kinds of sites that we saw in Yellow Birch; the two are common associates and competitors, much as Red Spruce and Balsam Fir repeatedly occur intermixed.

In the Adirondacks Red Maple is probably our most prolific sprouter. When the main stem is damaged, sprouts quickly appear from the old root collar. As many as six new stems, each a small tree, then compete with each other while nourished from the same root system; thus, one plant struggles with itself. When a forest region such as ours has been badly damaged, a vigorous species such as this grows in importance. Trees originating from sprout growth rarely become canopy dominants, however, because rot spreads quickly from the old decaying stump into the new root system.

Outwardly Red Maple seems to reproduce nearly as vigorously as Sugar Maple. The trees actually are less tolerant and, accord-

Red Maple. Red Maple when young soon develops concentric cracks in the bark, resembling a bull's eye target (left); then later breaks up into elongated strips that turn up at their ends like an exaggerated Eastern Hophornbeam (right). The round, red buds may be of help in identification when in doubt.

ingly, drop out quicker when they become shaded. On the other hand, once Red Maple does get established, it is a very fast grower, outreaching most of its associates.

Note that Red Maple leaves differ from Sugar Maple in two features: they are sharply toothed all along the edge, and the underside is a conspicuous white. In a slight breeze the whole tree looks silvery because of the upturned leaves. The leaf stalks even in mid-season are commonly tinged with red. The buds of Red Maple are just that—red—whereas Sugar Maple buds are dark brown. But it often takes a trained eye to catch the difference between the bark of the two trees. Red Maple becomes scaly when the trees reach diameters of about 6 inches; the pattern of these scales often resembles a bull's-eye with concentric cracks. In age both maples become deeply furrowed, the Red more so. In the fall the leaves of Red Maple are the most scarlet among all our hardwoods. If a branch is damaged for whatever reason during the summer months, the leaves on it will color prematurely, adding a spark of color to the green background. The paired, winged seeds of Sugar Maple are dropped in late summer, but on Red Maple they mature and fall about the time the leaves are fully expanded in late May or June.

One almost never has trouble locating a Red Maple to examine. A short walk in the woods will usually take you to one, an inconspicuous but abundant member of the surrounding forest greenery along low slope trails and flatlands, even spreading upslope to over 3000 feet after logging or wildfires. You also may encounter the closely related Silver Maple, *Acer saccharinum;* along that same section of the Ausable between Keene and Keene

Valley where we find the American Hornbeam and along the Saranac River in the northwest sector of the high peak region. The Silver Maple may be distinguished from the Red by its deeply dissected leaves, which make the resulting lobes more conspicuous. Both species are often multistemmed, apparently in part owing to deer browsing.

Key: gray bark developing patterns of concentric rings as bark becomes scaly, later entire trunk may become rough with vertically oriented scales turning outward at top and bottom as in hophornbeam but larger.

31. Striped Maple *Acer pennsylvanicum*

Much of the Striped Maple we see might better be classified as large shrubs rather than small trees, but since an occasional specimen does exceed 20 feet in height the species deserves mention here.

Striped Maple is an understory species of cool, moist, shaded spots. It is very tolerant of shade; in fact, it will not grow well where sunlight is strong. Trees grow best where sun flecks move across the ground during the day, but not where full sunlight floods the ground for any length of time. Birch and aspen provide a good canopy for Striped Maple, as on the lower sections of the MacIntyre trail a short distance above the Whale's Tail turn. Here the plants are tree-like, up to 20 feet in height with diameters of perhaps 4 or 5 inches. Trees of equal size occur on the trail up Mt. Jo and similar low-slope locations.

Striped Maple is an especially easy species to recognize. The leaves are quite large, averaging perhaps six inches long, shaped like a goose footprint with three long-pointed lobes and sharply toothed on the margins. The bark is a real eye-catcher: at first conspicuously bright green with vertical white stripes, whence the common name, the green bark fades each passing year toward a rusty brown characteristic of older growth. In similar fashion, each

Striped Maple. Trunks of Striped Maple are just that, vertically striped with green and white along their entire length. When they reach about 4" in diameter, the colors fade into light brown and gray but the smooth surface and the pattern persists into maturity.

October the green chlorophyll in the leaves disappears, revealing a hidden yellow accessory pigment, but that, too, fades as the leaves dry and fall to the ground later in the month. The absence of any red pigment is most unusual for a maple.

You may also find clumps of the shrub Mountain Maple nearby when you see Striped Maple. It has gray stems, many in a clump from one root system. The leaves are much smaller but the teeth much larger, and most leaves have five lobes instead of three.

Key: young bark greenish with white vertical stripes, in age darkening but stripes remaining evident.

32. American Basswood *Tilia americana*

American Basswood is more familiar to hikers in other sections of the state than it is to us in the high peak region. We are in the middle of the geographical range of the species, but the tree likes the warmer climates and richer soils at lower elevations within its range. Basswood in our area is found typically in the valleys, rarely on the slopes. Its distribution thus parallels that of Red Oak, Eastern Hophornbeam, White Ash and American Elm, all of which become abundant only on the mineral-rich soils of the Hardwood Site-Type. The highest I have seen trees growing is along the Johns Brook trail about a mile above the Garden parking area.

At the lower elevations basswood is the most vigorous sprouter, just as Red Maple is in the mountains proper. The species is easily recognized by its several trunks, each perhaps a foot in diameter, arising from one base. The individual stems may be quite straight

American Basswood. American Basswood at first has a smooth gray bark resembling White Ash, but it soon develops very steep fissures in the bark which thereby separate narrow flat ridges, vertically aligned. The pattern of distantly interconnected flat ridges persists into old age.

Mature trunks often have a ring of sprout around them, each of which may produce a new trunk when the parent tree is harvested.

and well-formed, though with a slight sweep to them. Being fairly tolerant of shade, the trees occur in mixture with a variety of other species, able to compete successfully with most of them.

Basswood leaves are broadly egg-shaped, about 5 or 6 inches long and nearly as wide, and sharply toothed on the margin. The leaf base is heart-shaped but lopsided, much as in elm leaves; if you fold a leaf along the midrib, the two sides do not match.

Key: smooth gray bark developing vertical, flat-topped ridges separated by narrow but steep-sided crevices.

33. White Ash *Fraxinus americana*

White Ash is one of our most valuable hardwoods. The wood is rated high for strength and ability to withstand shock, so it is one of the best species for use in sporting equipment, tool handles, and the like. The ecology of White Ash is similar to that of Black Cherry. Under primeval forest conditions it was an infrequent, perhaps rare, species. Because it is only intermediate in tolerance, ash is unable to invade mature stands where shade is heavy. But ever since vast areas of the Adirondacks were opened by farmers and the loggers, White Ash has come in strong as an important second-growth species and now occupies the canopy in many areas, though rarely in great numbers in any one spot. The best growth of White Ash is generally on the better sites where the soil is constantly moist, as along drainages and gentle slopes.

The higher one goes in the Adirondacks, the less the likelihood of seeing White Ash. It is primarily a species of lower elevation and level ground, as are basswood and Red Oak. The size of the trees varies with age, of course, but the largest are those found on sites opened up fairly early in the logging days. The largest specimen I know of (which also happens to be near the upper elevation limit of the species) is along the Johns Brook Trail at 1.43 miles;

White Ash. White Ash trees growing in the shade soon loose their side branches and devlop straight trunks with a characteristic bark pattern of close interconnected ridges, gray and rough on the surface.

one tree on the south edge of the trail is 3 feet in diameter. Most of our trees are about 60 or 70 feet tall at best and about 1½ feet in diameter. Farther south in the state, where White Ash is a common tree of woodlots, specimens are as tall and well-formed as any hardwood we have.

The bark of White Ash may be any one of three colors. Young trees in the open, exposed to the sun, have a smooth grayish bark tinged with orange or cinnamon. By the time trees reach a foot in diameter, the bark has roughened into a netlike pattern of ridges that are charcoal in color, almost as dark at times as Black Cherry. The old trees, nearly 2 feet or more in diameter and by now with wide, distantly interlacing ridges, have become an ordinary light gray. This variation in color and form of bark is more pronounced than in any other New York hardwood excepting Yellow Birch.

The ashes are our only tree with compound leaves arranged in opposite pairs. The leaves of White Ash are composed of seven leaflets, each egg-shaped to oblong in outline, each attached by its own tiny leafstalk, and relatively smooth on the margin. When teeth are present, they are confined to the forward section of the leaflet. In September, large clusters of narrow, winged seeds will be seen high in the crown. Notice that the twigs are slightly swollen at the nodes where the leaves arise, giving the twigs a knobby appearance. Because the leaves typically are spaced out on the branches, the crown of White Ash is quite open, somewhat as in intolerant pioneers such as aspen rather than climax species with dense foliage. This airiness of crown, along with the characteristic excellent form of the trees, places White Ash high on the list of preferred native species for either reforestation or ornamental use.

Key: young bark smooth, gray, somewhat cinnamon-colored, developing a pattern of vertical, intertwined ridges; in age developing long, flat-topped ridges separated by prominent crevices ending at bottom of crown.

34. Black Ash *Fraxinus nigra*

Black Ash is a species quite different from White Ash. A smaller tree, rarely over 40 feet tall, it is intolerant, and thus is found only where it gets lots of sunlight. It is strictly a wet-site species, confined to stream banks, swamps, and bogs where its roots are constantly bathed in free water. And although strictly a northern species, ranging even farther northward in Canada than American Beech and Sugar Maple, it is frequent in our region only at the lower elevations. In the high peak region Black Ash will be encountered only rarely, along the major watercourses, and rarely on the slopes. It is quite frequent on the riverbank terraces of the Ausable River just north of the trailhead to the North Notch Trail and is seen occasionally along the first section of that hiking trail.

Black Ash may be distinguished from White Ash by the larger leaves (often over a foot in length); by the number of leaflets (nine rather than seven, and each sessile rather than stalked); by the more oblong shape of each leaflet; and by the sharply toothed margin. In mid-summer clusters of small, yellowish-white winged seeds may be seen near the ends of the major limbs. The bark is always an intermediate dark gray, distinctly ridged and rough into the lower crown.

Black Ash. The bark of Black Ash differs from other Adirondack hardwoods in having indistinct vertical ridges that are so scaly as to obscure other features. Further, the rough pattern extends high up into the crown of the tree, where the thick, oppositely arranged branches and twigs verify it is an ash.

Black Ash has one specialty use: the making of pack baskets. The wood may be separated along the annual growth rings, thus providing sheets one-ring thick, ideal for cutting into narrow strips for weaving the baskets.

Key: bark soon roughening into dark, compact, intertwined ridges, extended upward into lower crown, reminiscent of American Elm.

The Evolving Conservation Ethic

Thirty years ago, when we talked of the "new conservation ethic" we spoke of the ever-increasing litter then appearing along trailsides, around lean-tos, and at scenic spots everywhere in the high peak wilderness. We urged climbers to leave the woods clean, free of litter and debris; to pack out whatever they had packed in. Individuals and organizations spoke as one on the matter: leave the forest as you would like to find it the next time you return: clean and attractive. That admonition still pertains, and the message was successful: the woods today are essentially clean of human refuse. The wilderness remains wild and aesthetically pleasing.

But a new and more serious problem has appeared, an ecological one, far more serious than the visual pollution of earlier times. By our very numbers we now are flooding the trail system, trampling the alpine meadows, crowding the tent sites, destroying the vegetation around scenic overlooks, and otherwise having a significant environmental impact on the very travel corridors and destinations we came to enjoy. We are loving the mountains and their forests and summits to death.

Fortunately, there are three possible resolutions to the dilemma: (1) reducing the number of people traversing the landscape; (2) educating the public to environmental awareness and appropriate personal behavior when visiting the wilderness; or (3) doing something about it ourselves individually to reduce the damage already inflicted on the natural resource we are utilizing.

Most folks do not want to deny the using public (the citizen owners) of their rights and their opportunity to enjoy their Adirondack forest preserve heritage, so option 1 is dismissed, at least for now.

Both options 2 and 3, though, are the current evolving conservation ethic, the old conservation ethic expanding to include personal, individual responsibility for avoiding activities that cause environmental degradation, while similarly working within our various organizations to take on a public service program, either of educating the hiking public or rehabilitating the damaged resource, or both. Witness the Department of Environmental Conservation (DEC) Summer Ranger Program wherein several young men and women hike the trails each day to advise or help ill-prepared hikers, assist in rescue efforts, or otherwise support the functions of the permanent DEC ranger force. Or the new Summit Stewardship program involving cooperative efforts among the Adirondack Nature Conservancy, the Adirondack Mountain Club, and the DEC, wherein a young steward serves as friendly host and educator on the two or three highest summits that now receive some 15,000 visitors each summer, a totally new phenomenon in wilderness management issues. Or the very successful efforts of the Adirondack Forty-sixers in stabilizing eroding trails in the high country and rehabilitating damaged alpine meadows, using the restoration procedures developed at the State University of New York College of Environmental Science and Forestry; and the tremendous improvements in the high peak region trail system and elsewhere by DEC-ADK trail crews working both with volunteers and paid employees. *All* these efforts reflect the evolving conservation ethic of wise use, of restoring the damaged forest environment, and educating the modern user to his or her personal responsibility for helping preserve our wilderness heritage here in the Adirondack high peaks.

The biggest, most dramatic change in public use in the peaks today is the evolving conservation ethic among those users who individually perform their own quiet public service simply by respecting the natural environment during their visit here. The future of the forests and trees is assured with that commitment.

Glossary

Acidic	Rocks or soils of low pH and fertility
Anorthosite	The coarse-grained bedrock that underlies the high peak region
Calcareous	Containing calcium carbonate and thereby producing fertile soil
Climax	Mature forest communities in a steady-state condition after succession is complete
DBH	Diameter Breast Height
Dominant	Trees that by their size and aggressiveness limit the growth of associated species
Esker	A long, winding and narrow ridge of stony glacial moraine, often several miles long, left by the retreating glaciers
Flagging	The lopsided effect created when trees grow on exposed sites where prevailing winds contort the foliage toward the leeward side of the crown
Forest type	One or more species that alone or in combination form stands repeating themselves across the region; may be either successional (temporary) or climax (permanent)
Intolerant	Species unable to prosper in shade because they require full sunlight for growth

Moraine	Stony and coarse-grained glacial till left by glacial melt-waters
Muskeg	Permanent bogs at high latitudes where only black spruce and tamarack survive
pH	A numerical measure of acidity; 7 is neutral, less than 7 is acidic, more than 7 is alkaline
Pioneer	A species that appears early in plant succession while full sunlight bathes the site
Plant succession	The series of changing plant populations that gradually over time convert open land into mature plant communities
Pleistocene	The glacial period that ended approximately 14,000 years ago
Site-type	One of five environmental conditions in the Adirondacks wherein successional trends converge toward a characteristic combination of climax tree species
Taiga	The stunted coniferous/evergreen landscape of cold, high latitudes
Till	The unsorted glacial debris left by a retreating glacier, generally fertile with all sizes of soil particles present
Tolerant	Able to prosper in shade, as in mature forests
Water-washed	Referring to glacial till from which the silts and clays have been washed out by melt water during glacial retreat
YBP	Years before present

Checklist

Species	A	B	C	D	E	F	G	H	I	J	K	L
	Locations*											
1. Eastern White Pine	○	○	○	○	○	○	○	○	○	○	○	○
2. Red Pine	○	○	○	○	○	○	○	○	○	○	○	○
3. Jack Pine	○	○	○	○	○	○	○	○	○	○	○	○
4. Pitch Pine	○	○	○	○	○	○	○	○	○	○	○	○
5. Scotch Pine	○	○	○	○	○	○	○	○	○	○	○	○
6. Tamarack	○	○	○	○	○	○	○	○	○	○	○	○
7. Eastern Hemlock	○	○	○	○	○	○	○	○	○	○	○	○
8. Red Spruce	○	○	○	○	○	○	○	○	○	○	○	○
9. Black Spruce	○	○	○	○	○	○	○	○	○	○	○	○
10. White Spruce	○	○	○	○	○	○	○	○	○	○	○	○
11. Norway Spruce	○	○	○	○	○	○	○	○	○	○	○	○
12. Balsam Fir	○	○	○	○	○	○	○	○	○	○	○	○
13. Northern White-cedar	○	○	○	○	○	○	○	○	○	○	○	○
14. Eastern Redcedar	○	○	○	○	○	○	○	○	○	○	○	○
15. Quaking Aspen	○	○	○	○	○	○	○	○	○	○	○	○
16. Bigtooth Aspen	○	○	○	○	○	○	○	○	○	○	○	○

	A	B	C	D	E	F	G	H	I	J	K	L
17. Balsam Poplar	○	○	○	○	○	○	○	○	○	○	○	○
18. Eastern Hophornbeam	○	○	○	○	○	○	○	○	○	○	○	○
19. Paper Birch	○	○	○	○	○	○	○	○	○	○	○	○
20. Yellow Birch	○	○	○	○	○	○	○	○	○	○	○	○
21. Gray Birch	○	○	○	○	○	○	○	○	○	○	○	○
22. American Beech	○	○	○	○	○	○	○	○	○	○	○	○
23. Northern Red Oak	○	○	○	○	○	○	○	○	○	○	○	○
24. American Elm	○	○	○	○	○	○	○	○	○	○	○	○
25. American Mountain-ash	○	○	○	○	○	○	○	○	○	○	○	○
26. Black Cherry	○	○	○	○	○	○	○	○	○	○	○	○
27. Fire Cherry	○	○	○	○	○	○	○	○	○	○	○	○
28. Shadbush	○	○	○	○	○	○	○	○	○	○	○	○
29. Sugar Maple	○	○	○	○	○	○	○	○	○	○	○	○
30. Red Maple	○	○	○	○	○	○	○	○	○	○	○	○
31. Striped Maple	○	○	○	○	○	○	○	○	○	○	○	○
32. American Basswood	○	○	○	○	○	○	○	○	○	○	○	○
33. White Ash	○	○	○	○	○	○	○	○	○	○	○	○
34. Black Ash	○	○	○	○	○	○	○	○	○	○	○	○

**List locations on page 162.*

*List locations below where species were found:

A. ______________________________

B. ______________________________

C. ______________________________

D. ______________________________

E. ______________________________

F. ______________________________

G. ______________________________

H. ______________________________

I. ______________________________

J. ______________________________

K. ______________________________

L. ______________________________

Epilogue

My account of the forests and trees of the Adirondack high peak region has been necessarily brief and incomplete. I hope that the end of this account will be for you the beginning of a long-lasting interest in the forested Adirondack high country.

As an avocation, the study of trees never really ends. There are always a few more species to find, some detail to examine more closely, some countryside to explore, varying forest stands to visit and interpret. Reading the landscape adds a new dimension to any Adirondack experience. On every climb you are essentially walking through history, ancient and modern, a story recorded in the condition of the forest and in the kinds of trees present. During July and August the resident ranger-naturalist of the Adirondack Mountain Club at Adirondak Loj will gladly assist you with your questions. At other times feel free to send your "problem specimens" or whatever forest or tree questions you may have to Dr. E.H. Ketchledge, c/o Adirondack Mountain Club, 814 Goggins Road, Lake George, NY 12845-4117.

Dr. E.H. Ketchledge
August 1996

Notes

Notes

Notes

Notes

Notes

JOIN US!

We are a nonprofit membership organization that brings together people with interests in recreation, conservation, and environmental education in the New York State Forest Preserve.

Membership Rewards

Discovery

ADK can broaden your horizons by introducing you to new people, new places, recreational activities and interests.

Member Benefits

- 20% discount on all ADK publications, including guidebooks and maps
- 10% discount on ADK lodging facilities in the Adirondacks
- 10% discount on ADK logo merchandise
- Reduced rates for educational programs
- One-year subscription to *Adirondac* magazine
- Membership in one of ADK's 26 chapters
- Member-only outings to exciting destinations around the world

Satisfaction

Knowing you're doing your part to protect and preserve our mountains, rivers, forests and lakes to ensure that future generations will be able to enjoy the wilderness as we have.

JOIN A CHAPTER

Three-quarters of ADK members belong to a local chapter. Those not wishing to join a particular chapter may join ADK as members-at-large.

Chapter membership brings you the fun of outings and social activities and the reward of working on trails, conservation, and education projects at the local level. Chapter membership is included in your benefits.

Adirondak Loj .... North Elba
Albany .... Albany
Algonquin .... Plattsburgh
Black River .... Watertown
Cold River .... Long Lake
Finger Lakes .... Ithaca–Elmira
Genesee Valley .... Rochester
Glens Falls .... Glens Falls
Hurricane Mountain .... Keene
Iroquois .... Utica
Keene Valley .... Keene Valley
Knickerbocker .... New York City and vicinity
Lake Placid .... Lake Placid
Laurentian .... Canton-Potsdam
Long Island .... Long Island
Mid-Hudson .... Dutchess Co.
Mohican .... Westchester and Putnam Counties, NY/Fairfield Co., CT
New York .... Metropolitan Area*
Niagara Frontier .... Buffalo
North Jersey .... Bergen County
North Woods .... Saranac Lake–Tupper Lake
Onondaga .... Syracuse
Ramapo .... Rockland & Orange Counties
Schenectady .... Schenectady
Shatagee Woods .... Malone
Susquehanna .... Oneonta

**Special requirements apply*

Your membership is not limited to one chapter. You may affiliate with as many chapters as you like for a small fee (the cost of the newsletter).

MEMBERSHIP

To Join

Call **1-800-395-8080** or send this form with payment to

Adirondack Mountain Club
814 Goggins Rd.
Lake George, NY 12845-4117.

Check Membership Level:

☐	Patron	$160*
☐	Supporting	$80*
☐	Family	$45*
☐	Adult	$40
☐	Senior Family	$35*
☐	Senior (65+)	$30
☐	Junior (under 18)	$25
☐	Student (18+, full time)	$25

School ______________________

**Includes associate/family members*

Name ______________________

Address ______________________

City ______________ State _____ Zip _______

Home Telephone (   ) ______________

☐ I want to join as a member-at-large.

☐ I want to join as a ______________ Chapter member.

(For more information on Chapters, call 518-668-4447, ext. 30.)

List spouse & children under 18 with birthdates:

Spouse ______________________

Child ______________ Birthdate __________

Child ______________ Birthdate __________

Bill my: ☐ VISA ☐ MASTERCARD ☐ DISCOVER ☐ AM. EX

Expiration Date ____________

|_|_|_|_|_|_|_|_|_|_|_|_|_|_|_|_|

____
Signature (required for charge)

Adirondack ADK Mountain Club

ADK is a nonprofit, tax-exempt organization. Membership fees are tax deductible, as allowed by law. Please allow 6–8 weeks for receipt of first issue of **Adirondac**.

All fees subject to change.

FT

Backdoor to Backcountry

ADK outings and workshops—there's one just right for you!

ADK offers friendly outings for all skill levels—for those just getting started in local chapters, to Adirondack bushwhacks and international treks. Learn gradually through chapter outings or attend one of our schools, workshops, or other programs. A sampling includes:

- Alpine Flora
- Ice Climbing
- Rock Climbing
- Basic Canoeing
- Bicycle Touring
- Cross-country Skiing
- Mountain Photography
- Winter Mountaineering
- Birds of the Adirondacks
- Geology of the High Peaks

... and so much more!

For more about our workshops:

ADK Education Department
P.O. Box 867, Lake Placid, NY 12946
(518) 523-3441 9:00 a.m.–7:00 p.m.

For information about the Adirondacks or about ADK:

ADK's Information Center & Headquarters
814 Goggins Road, Lake George, NY 12845-4117
(518) 668-4447
Exit 21 off I-87 ("the Northway"), 9N South

May–December: Mon.–Sat., 8:30 a.m.–5:00 p.m.
January–April: Mon.–Fri., 8:30 a.m.–5:00 p.m.

To join ADK by credit card, please call our toll-free number: 800-395-8080 (8:30 a.m.–5:00 p.m., M–F). Callers who join may take immediate discounts on ADK publications, workshops, ADK logo merchandise and lodge rates and may charge all to Visa, Mastercard, Discover or American Express.

For information about ADK lodge, cabin, or campground sites on ADK's Heart Lake property in the High Peaks:

ADK Lodges, PO Box 867, Lake Placid, NY 12946
(518) 523-3441 9 a.m.–7:00 p.m.

Visit our web site: www.adk.org

The Adirondack Mountain Club, Inc.
814 Goggins Road, Lake George, NY 12845-4117
(518) 668-4447/Orders only: 800-395-8080 (M–F, 8:30–5:00)

BOOKS

85 Acres: A Field Guide to the Adirondack Alpine Summits
Adirondack Canoe Waters: North Flow
Adirondack Canoe Waters: South & West Flow
The Adirondack Mt. Club Canoe Guide to Western & Central New York State
Adirondack Park Mountain Bike Preliminary Trail and Route Listing
An Adirondack Passage: The Cruise of the Canoe *Sairy Gamp*
The Adirondack Reader
Adirondack Wildguide (distributed by ADK)
An Adirondack Sampler I: Day Hikes for All Seasons
An Adirondack Sampler II: Backpacking Trips
Classic Adirondack Ski Tours
Climbing in the Adirondacks: A Guide to Rock & Ice Routes
Forests & Trees of the Adirondack High Peaks Region
Guide to Adirondack Trails: High Peaks Region
Guide to Adirondack Trails: Northern Region
Guide to Adirondack Trails: Central Region
Guide to Adirondack Trails: Northville–Placid Trail
Guide to Adirondack Trails: West-Central Region
Guide to Adirondack Trails: Eastern Region
Guide to Adirondack Trails: Southern Region
Guide to Catskill Trails
Kids on the Trail! Hiking with Children in the Adirondacks
Our Wilderness: How the People of New York Found,
Changed, and Preserved the Adirondacks
Trailside Notes: A Naturalist's Companion to Adirondack Plants
Winterwise: A Backpacker's Guide
With Wilderness at Heart: A Short History of the Adirondack Mountain Club

MAPS

Trails of the High Peaks Region
Trails of the Northern Region
Trails of the Central Region
The Northville–Placid Trail
Trails of the West-Central Region
Trails of the Eastern Region
Trails of the Southern Region

Price list available on request.